THE MAUI BOOK OF
LAVENDER

THE MAUI BOOK OF
LAVENDER

ALII CHANG • LANI MEDINA WEIGERT • JILL ENGLEDOW

WATERMARK
PUBLISHING

ISBN 978-0-9790647-7-7

Library of Congress Control Number: 2008938684

Design
Leo Gonzalez
Marisa Oshiro

Photography
J. Anthony Martinez
Peter Liu
James Page

Culinary photography
Adriana Torres Chong

Additional photography
Jill Engledow, 8,9
Hawai'i State Archives, 11
Dreamstime.com, 31, 103, 105
iStock.com, 5,6,7
Greg Hoxie, 41

Information in this book is not meant to provide individual medical advice. No treatment or product herein is intended to diagnose, prevent or cure any disease or other malady. Readers should verify for themselves the accuracy of any recommendations or other information before making decisions regarding health care or treatment.

Watermark Publishing
1088 Bishop St., Suite 310
Honolulu, Hawaii 96813
Telephone 1-808-587-7766
Toll-free 1-866-900-BOOK
sales@bookshawaii.net
www.bookshawaii.net

Printed in China

CONTENTS

igh on the slopes of Haleakalā, Aliʻi Kula Lavender blossoms amidst rolling green pastures. The air is scented with the fragrance of lavender, a plant with a long history that has found a new home on this Maui farm. Here it grows in a setting like a real-life Monet painting, a dreamlike palette of pastels. Lavender plants stretch in undulating rows across the hillside, their silvery mounds topped with purple flowers. A dragonfly with iridescent wings hovers near a garden pond. High above, birds swoop and sing in the peaceful Kula sky. Below, the shining sea stretches to the horizon, and across the isthmus of Central Maui, clouds crown the peaks of the West Maui mountains.

This lovely place is home not only to the lavender plant, with its legendary scent and astonishing array of uses, but to a thriving business that flourishes because it helps its neighbors to thrive as well. Forty-five varieties of lavender and 55,000 plants grow at Aliʻi Kula Lavender. But what is truly blossoming are the people who are part of the experience, both those who work there and those who visit.

The lessons learned in farming lavender are rich in metaphor and lend themselves naturally to parallel lessons about growing your dreams and nurturing their fulfillment. Lofty as that sounds, sometimes the first step is simply being awakened to opportunities in front of you. That's how it started for the people on this farm. For another farmer, the opportunity might be found in a crop of corn, tomatoes or watermelon. In your life, the opportunities might be altogether different. When your moment comes, remember that change is not always bad, innovation is key and having faith and belief in your vision is essential.

So, yes, this is a story about the wonderful lavender plant and about a lavender farm on Maui. But it is just as much about listening: listening to the land, listening to your heart, listening to your market. It is a book about a journey that manifests its spirit through growing and nurturing all living things, through collaboration, inclusion, creativity and the belief in things greater than us. This is a book about nurturing your spirit as it relates to working and being connected to the land. By coming back to the land, we are re-connected to our source, to each other and ultimately to ourselves. ⊙ϟϟ~

"THE KISS OF THE SUN FOR PARDON,
THE SONG OF THE BIRDS FOR MIRTH,
ONE IS NEARER GOD'S HEART IN A GARDEN
THAN ANYWHERE ELSE ON EARTH."

—DOROTHY FRANCES GURNEY
GARDEN THOUGHTS

CHAPTER ONE

The Story of Lavender

"ALTHOUGH HUMAN SUBTLETY MAKES A VARIETY OF INVENTIONS
BY DIFFERENT MEANS TO THE SAME END, IT WILL NEVER DEVISE
AN INVENTION MORE BEAUTIFUL, MORE SIMPLE, OR MORE DIRECT
THAN DOES NATURE, BECAUSE IN HER INVENTIONS NOTHING IS
LACKING, AND NOTHING IS SUPERFLUOUS."

LEONARDO DA VINCI

*P*art of the charm of this useful herb is that it benefits the humble as well as the highborn. Once upon a time, no herb garden was without lavender, no home without its fragrance and no healer without its products.

The use of lavender has been recorded for more than 2,500 years, and chances are its beneficial qualities were recognized long before that by human beings seeking relief from their ailments and a sweet scent in a world without soaps and lotions. By trial and error, the properties of lavender, and other herbs, were learned and passed on from one generation to the next. Today, in an increasingly artificial society, people who crave a more natural lifestyle often turn to the herbs their ancestors relied upon. And in the case of lavender, scientific research has proven the effectiveness of many of the herb's traditional treatments.

With such a long history and an incredibly wide range of uses, there are many stories about lavender.

The herb is native to the mountainous zones around the Mediterranean, where it grows in sunny, stony habitats. It may have originally come from farther east, in Mesopotamia (currently Iraq), but it has also long grown wild in southern Europe. The use of lavender was documented by Pedanius Dioscorides, a practicing physician, botanist and pharmacologist in Rome at the time of the Emperor Nero. Dioscorides wrote one of the most influential herbal books in history, titled *De Materia Medica*. In his manuscript, the physician called lavender a "precious plant." Following his advice, Roman soldiers carried lavender oil in their first-aid kits. The Romans and Greeks also used lavender in their bath water, both for its fragrance and its disinfecting power. The plant's name comes from the Latin— either *lavare* (to wash), or *livendula* (leaden-blue or bluish).

The Egyptians used lavender as part of their mummification process, but apparently they also knew that lavender's scent is enticing to men who are still alive. Cleopatra, for instance, reportedly used a lavender perfume to help her seduce both Julius Caesar and Marc Anthony.

> *"Flowers ... are a proud assertion that a ray of beauty out values all the utilities of the world."*
>
> RALPH WALDO EMERSON

By around 600 A.D., lavender spread to the highlands of France, where it thrived in what would become today's world lavender capital—Provence.

As the Dark Ages closed in, the scientific learning pursued by the Greeks and Romans came to a halt. However, monasteries and herb gardeners continued to embrace lavender and other herbs, planting gardens and preserving the literature of medical and herbal practices. Monks grew medicinal herbs in order to tend to the sick as part of their Christian duty. Benedictine abbess St. Hildegard von Bingen described many medicinal recipes, including a tincture of lavender, with vodka or brandy, to rub over the temples as treatment for migraines. No doubt, ordinary folk also grew the traditional herbs in their cottage gardens, and "green men and women," wise in the ways of the woods, harvested wild plants to sell to apothecaries who prepared them for medicinal use.

Lavender is famous for its clean, sweet smell, and its cleansing and disinfecting agents were important in Medieval and Renaissance Europe. Washerwomen known as "lavenders" used the herb to scent linen drawers and cabinets. They also dried laundry on lavender bushes planted near the washroom door. Housewives tucked lavender into their cupboards, burned its branches to clear the air in sick rooms and washed walls with lavender water. In the days when floors were carpeted with a layer of straw called rushes, women strewed their floors with lavender, thus deodorizing the room and repelling the insects that bite animals and humans alike.

Travelers put together little bouquets that came to be called tussie-mussies—sweet-scented nosegays they could carry to ward off bad odors and infection.

For more than 15 centuries, lavender has been cultivated and celebrated in France and throughout Europe.

Lavender's insect repellent property was a lifesaver in times of plague, when thousands died of the disease we now know was spread by infected fleas. One famous story tells of four thieves who were caught ransacking the empty houses—and even graves—of plague victims after the bubonic plague struck Marseille, France. When the judge inquired about how they had resisted the plague, they confessed that they had drunk and washed with a lavender-vinegar concoction. The men were freed in exchange for the recipe. During subsequent episodes of plague, many people soaked sponges in "Four

Thieves Vinegar" which, held to the nose, were thought to repel the disease. In England, bunches of lavender fastened to each wrist helped protect the wearer, and French glovemakers who perfumed their wares with lavender remained healthy through epidemics.

It is not clear how lavender made its way to England; it may have traveled with the Romans or arrived later when the Norman conquerors came from France. At any rate, it was soon used in a wide variety of foods and was a particular favorite of Queen Elizabeth I. Her Majesty had a sweet tooth, and it is said that she kept a conserve of lavender (a mixture of lavender flowers and sugar) on her dining table and drank sweet lavender tisane, a hot tea made with lavender flowers and honey. William Turner, the father of English botany and author of the first major book about plants written in English, *The New Herballe*, dedicated the work to the queen in 1568. One of Turner's comments echoes the modern understanding of lavender as a headache remedy: "I judge that the flowers of lavender quilted in a cap and dayly worne are good for all diseases of the head that come from a cold cause and that they comfort the braine very well."

By 1652, Nicholas Culpeper wrote in his book, *The English physisian: or an astrologo-physical discourse of the vulgar herbs of this nation*, that lavender "is so wel known, being an Inhabitant in almost every Garden, that it needeth no Description."

By the 1820s, lavender was commercially cultivated in England, and the famous perfumery company Yardley began making lavender

The hill country of Provence in southeastern France is recognized as the world capital of lavender.

soaps and perfumes. Queen Victoria was another great lover of lavender. It is said that her husband Prince Albert courted her with lavender bouquets. Lavender was a major component in smelling salts, used to revive swooning ladies. The scent was so popular in Victorian times that its overuse actually made it disliked. By the 20th century, lavender was associated with grandma, and for a time it fell out of fashion. Still, lavender remained an ingredient in many perfumes made of a mixture of scents.

Lavender traveled from Europe to America with the earliest settlers and was commercially grown for medicinal purposes by the Shakers, a Protestant religious denomination. Since this group was celibate, its members probably paid no mind to the sensual and alleged aphrodisiac properties of the herb, focusing instead on its many practical uses.

Lavender, and many other healing herbs, have always had a place in folk medicine. As science surged ahead, researchers began distilling herbs and pin-pointing the active ingredients in their essential oils.

As the world turned from natural remedies to syn-thetic medicines, it took an accident in a French perfume laboratory to bring the original herbal products back to the limelight. In the early 1900s, chemist Rene-Maurice Gattefossé burned himself badly while working in his family's perfume business. Instinctively, he plunged his burned arm into the nearest liquid, which happened be lavender oil, rather than water. To his surprise, the burn healed with remarkable speed and left no scars. Gat-tefossé coined the term "aromatherapy" and became the father of the "French model" of aromatherapy, in which essential oils are used intensively in and on the body, like any medicine.

Today lavender's essential oils are put to a variety of uses.

A French physician, Dr. Jean Valnet, resorted to oils when he ran out of antibiotics while treating injured soldiers during World War II and found them surprisingly effective. He continued to develop aromatherapy upon the foundation laid by Gattefossé.

By the turn of the 21st century, lavender covered the hills of Provence, where most of the world's lavender oil is produced. In the United States, Oregon was home to lavender farms that produced a range of products for health, beauty and culinary use. In Sequim, Washington, an agricultural community faced with declining farms and the development of farmlands pulled together to create a new lavender industry. In Australia and New Zealand, Spain and England, purple fields flourished as lavender's popularity bloomed once again.

Lavender in The Islands

A lavender bush grows by the front door at Honolulu's Mission Houses Museum, just where it might have grown when the building was home to early-19th century Protestant missionaries.

No one seems to know how or when lavender first found its way to Hawai'i. Perhaps no one recorded its introduction because it was such a common household item by the 1800s. After all, who would write a journal entry about having soap or sugar on hand? By the time American Protestant and French Catholic missionaries arrived in the Islands, lavender was so commonly used in America and Europe that it was on a par with these other daily staples. We know that the American missionaries who came to Hawai'i from the Mainland brought other heritage plants like the rose, but we can only assume that they also planted lavender. Nearly two centuries after their arrival, the first home these missionaries built (now part of the Mission Houses Museum in downtown Honolulu) had a lavender plant growing by its doorstep—just where a hardworking housewife of that time would have wanted that handy herb to grow.

And we know the mission families used lavender, whether homegrown or imported. In a letter written in 1849, missionary Amos Starr Cooke mentioned that, "Last night our dear Juliette was afflicted with palpitation, but a spoonful of 'Lavender' soon relieved her."

Another early piece of evidence of lavender in Hawai'i is found in 1849 newspaper advertisements in the *Honolulu Times*. Lavender water, along with an assortment of goods—ranging from ladies' white silk stockings to pickles—was among the merchandise for sale by merchants J.J. Caranave and Crabb & Spalding. Twenty years later, in 1869, the Hawaiian language paper *Ke Au Okoa* printed an ad for M. McInerny, whose store would be a Honolulu institution until the late 20th century, advertising *ka wai lavender maikai* (fine lavender water) and *ka lavender boke hoikeike* (a lavender bouquet for display).

Just a year later, *Ke Au Okoa* printed the words to a song about lavender by a composer identified as "Mr. Bone." As in many songs of the time, the writer sprinkled a few English words here and there. The "sweet lavender flower" is probably a reference to the lyricist's beloved. Liliko'i is a place in East Maui, where it is said the fruit was first grown.

Hawai'i's Queen Lili'uokalani recorded this list of trees and flowers, including a lavender bush, growing on the grounds of Washington Place, her home in Honolulu.

Pua Lavender

He halia ka i hiki mai,
Koni ana i ka puuwai,
Loku ana i ka houpo,
No ka pua sweet Lavender.

Chorus:
Hu wale mai ke aloha,
Ka haupu me ka halia,
No ia la no kuu hoa,
No ka pua sweet Lavender.

Hoohihi aku ka manao,
I ka malu hekuawa,
Maua pu me ia la,
Me ka pua sweet Lavender.

(Chorus)

Kau nui aku e ike.
I ka lai o Lilikoi,
E walea ai maua,
Me ka pua sweet Lavender.

(Chorus)

Me oe ko'u aloha,
E ka nani oia uka,
Good bye! Good bye! kaua;
E ka pua sweet Lavender.

(Chorus)

Lavender Flower

The memories come back to me,
Throbbing in the heart,
Love is surging in the chest,
For the sweet Lavender flower.

Chorus:
Love is rising to the surface,
The memory and the fond recollection,
Of this day, of my beloved friend,
Of the sweet Lavender flower.

The thoughts that come are like a vow
made in the valley shade,
The two of us are together this day,
With the sweet Lavender flower.

(Chorus)

Place yourself in the calm of Liliko'i.
And see the two of us,
Relaxed and at ease,
With the sweet Lavender flower.

(Chorus)

My aloha is with you,
By the beauty of the uplands,
The two of us say farewell;
The sweet lavender flower.

(Chorus)

Opposite is the song in Hawaiian and English, translated by Frank Kawaikapuokalani Hewett. Hawaiian writers of that time did not use the diacritical marks now added to aid pronunciation and clarify meaning, and this song is printed here as it was in *Ke Au Okoa*, with only a single *'okina* in the word *ko'u*.

In addition to these written fragments that prove lavender was known and loved in Hawai'i, other tantalizing clues indicate that it was well used here less than a century after the first Western contact.

Kama'aina (native-born) recall family stories about the pervasive scent of lavender in daily life, from lavender water on pocket handkerchiefs to sachets tucked into linen closets.

Lavender also fit right into the regal Victorian atmosphere of 'Iolani Palace, where Hawai'i's monarchs lived during the 1800s. Many of Hawai'i's royals were anglophiles, and several of them visited England. Queen Emma traveled to London in 1865 to meet lavender lover Queen Victoria, and corresponded with her for years. King Kalākaua, the first monarch ever to travel around the world, called on Queen Victoria in 1881. Young Princess Ka'iulani, the presumed heir to

Island royalty, including King Kalākaua, admired all things English during lavender's heyday in the late 19th century.

the throne of Queen Lili'uokalani, attended finishing school in Northampton-shire, England. With Hawai'i admiring all things English during lavender's heyday, it only takes a bit of imagination to visualize Hawai'i's royalty using lavender just as the gentlefolk of England did. In fact, Lili'uokalani, Hawai'i's last queen, listed "lavender bush" on the handwritten inventory she made of the trees and flowers growing at her home, Washington Place.

A century later, a creative and enterprising farmer on Maui discovered that this Mediterranean native was a perfect transplant to the slopes of the great mountain called Haleakalā.

Ali'i Kula Lavender's Alii Chang: "I think the lavender chose me."

The Roots of Ali'i Kula Lavender

"My passion has always been in the earth," says Alii Chang, who planted a lavender farm in Upcountry Maui and made it into a work of art.

Alii Chang comes by his green thumb naturally. He grew up on a 20-acre farm in Kāne'ohe, on the fertile wind-ward side of O'ahu. He watched and learned from his grand-mother, who could grow anything and who had a recipe for every crop. From breadfruit chips to mango cobbler to pickled star fruit, she turned the gifts of the land into deli-cious dishes. Her gardening and her enterprising spirit left an indelible imprint on the little boy who tagged along, learning to help his grand-mother work the farm.

"Nothing is more the child of art than a garden."

SIR WALTER SCOTT

This grandmother, Chris-tina Lamson (aka Lani), took the little boy to live with her under the Hawaiian custom known as *hānai*, in which family members informally adopt children. Alii was the second of 16 children born to his mother; later his father remarried and fathered eight more. "My father was charming, but he was not a businessperson," Alii recalls. In his parents' home children were expected to follow the Hawaiian tradition of obedience without asking questions. This was difficult for a boy who always wanted to know "why."

His grandmother was entirely different. She was tough but gracious, outspoken and aristocratic. Though her ancestry included Hawaiian and Chinese, her take on life came from her English and German ancestors, who had a direct approach and a strong business orientation. "I want you to speak up," Grandma said, encouraging questions. "I'm going to teach you how to do things businesslike."

"We got along so well," Alii says. "Somehow we matched each other, and I just loved her garden. She bottled or pickled everything, and what we didn't use went into the compost pile. Everything produced heavily for us."

The 20 acres of fruit trees, with flowers planted at their bases, were farmed organically and fertilized with seaweed and chicken manure. And while there was no time to be idle, his grandmother encouraged Alii's creativity. "She made me express art in whatever I did," he says.

In school he excelled in art and agriculture. At home on the farm, he was surrounded by his grandmother's orchids and antiques, and she made sure he learned table manners and other social graces. The boy's soul and his artistic tendencies grew in tandem, along

As the early days rolled by, my time spent with Alii increased and so did my enthusiasm for this magical place and its potential. Walking with Alii through the farm, I'd listen to the many stories he had to share about his childhood and subsequent 40 years as a farmer. As he spoke, I had the uncanny feeling that I knew these stories, that my eerily familiar connection to Alii spanned lifetimes. It felt like I was coming home. Not only were his stories compelling, but so was his telling of them. Though his passion for the land and for all living things was irrefutable, this was a man with a lighthearted touch who was quick to laugh, and that childlike spirit was contagious.

—Lani Medina Weigert

with his agricultural skills.

Grandma taught Alii how to prune, sending him up into enormous mango trees wielding a handsaw. She stood below with a rope tied to the branch to

control its fall and protect the flowers below. She taught him how to bargain for the best price for a product. Alii says that it was an exciting time when the buyers came from Chinatown to purchase the precious lychee fruit. He remembers, "Watching Grandma and the Chinese fight over the price was a show in itself."

Grandma Lani died about the time Alii graduated from high school, leaving a legacy of skills and knowledge that would serve him throughout life. The young man continued his education at business college and studied hotel and restaurant management. "I had to learn quickly, because I was on my own," Alii says. "I was determined to be successful. I didn't mind working hard, because everything I did I had a passion for. I dreamed big."

Alii was making his living as a landscaper. The work felt to him more like creating pieces of art than running a business. But the young man had the advantage of the business skills he had learned from his grandmother. When he bought his first house, he paid for the house in cash and didn't take out a mortgage. As a new homeowner, he landscaped his own yard. His work impressed the neighbors, who wanted to hire him to design their gardens, too. Meanwhile, he fixed up his first home, sold it, moved to another and did the same. He moved every six months, buying all his real estate with cash.

The landscaping business was good, but Alii decided to cut it back to a side job when a new opportunity came up—working as a deckhand on a tour boat. This job led to a sales position that allowed him to travel, seeing the world for several years as he represented the boat company at travel conventions. When the sales job began to require too much entertaining and partying for Alii's taste, he knew where to go: back to his first love, the land.

He decided to buy land where he could raise landscape plants, and opened the first Alii Gardens in a gated community on Windward O'ahu. When the neighborhood protested having a business in the community, he sold the land, made a profit and bought 2.5 acres in

The climate and soil conditions on Haleakalā's leeward flank created an ideal setting for the future lavender farm.

Pūpūkea on Oʻahu's North Shore. When the Kuilima Hotel opened nearby, with 500 rooms to be decorated, he bid on the hotel's floral design contract.

"They wanted blooming bougainvillea in every room. I never said no! I just went for it. It was my biggest job yet," Alii says. "I had never done a grand opening in my life."

Luckily, his landscaping business gave him access to bougainvillea in gallon-sized containers, and he had lauhala hats custom made to hold the pots. He recalls, "All the lobbies were done in exotic tropicals no one had ever seen before—bromeliads, heliconias and banana flowers—with a stunning 19-foot arrangement near the elevator."

In June 2002 Alii planted the first 5,000 lavender "starts" on his newly purchased acreage in Kula.

The opening was such a success that Alii took over the hotel's flower shop, and soon had a rotating staff working 20 hours every day. They made hundreds of lei to greet guests and decorated lavish banquets and special events. He says, "It was such a high. It was like being in show biz!"

But such success took its toll, and Alii was ready for something new. His next move took him to Maui, where a friend had offered to sell him land she owned in Nāhiku. "If anyone can do something with this land, it would be you," she said. Alii already knew what he would grow. He had tried to keep up with his shop's increasing demand by raising exotic tropicals on his Pūpūkea land, but couldn't produce enough even for his own operation. In Nāhiku, he would go back to the land full-time as a grower of exotics and become a supplier for a floral trend he had himself helped to develop.

In March 1976, Alii Gardens opened at Nāhiku, an isolated community along the winding Hana Highway on the rainy eastern coast of Maui. There was no piped water or electricity on this verdant 60 acres, but Alii built a water catchment system with his roof and a large tank, which the rain kept full. This jungle land was perfect for growing tropical ornamental plants.

Alii began working with a long-time Hana farmer, Howard Cooper of Helani Gardens, to propagate, grow and market these exotic flowers. Soon, the green Nāhiku jungle was bright with colorful ginger and heliconia. Howard was a connoisseur of plants, while Alii brought marketing skills. The two gardening pioneers found a ready market for their blooms, exporting them around the globe. "We started the tropical heliconia craze," Alii says. "We kind of fed each other's frenzy."

Trading cuttings of brilliant and wonderful new cultivars, they established an industry that would become

Alii Kula Lavender's first farm tours were a harbinger of bigger things to come—the fast-growing industry now known as agri-tourism.

a mainstay of the Hana area. The duo made up new names for their plants—the "sexy pink" heliconia, a name they thought up one night over cocktails, or the "birdiana" for a plant that just appeared in the field, its seed perhaps dropped by a passing bird.

Busy exporting flowers all over the world, Alii finally agreed to repeated requests for an interview—a story in American Airlines' *American Way* magazine. "This is going to be as-is conditions," he warned the writer, who wanted to spend a week living on the farm. "I get up at 4:30 in the morning." The resulting cover story brought even more orders. "I couldn't keep up with all the demands."

By 1989, his business had once again grown too big for comfort. Alii sold the garden to a Japanese company, but stayed on to run the farm. When he finally left three years later, he signed a non-compete clause that prohibited him from growing tropical flowers anywhere in the state for five years.

But Alii is not a man who can sit still. Already he had bought part of a former Kula protea farm. "Somehow, I was attracted to this place," he says. "I looked at many places, and this was the only one I wanted." He settled in and began to think about what he could grow in the cool Upcountry climate, so different from the humid warmth of Nāhiku. Up a narrow country road, with a comfortable and pleasant farmhouse, Alii's new home was already a garden, filled with the flowers that had become one of Kula's signature crops—the protea, a native of South Africa. As he enjoyed his new home and puttered in the garden, Alii also took on a new challenge, buying a seven-unit vacation rental business in the beach community of Kīhei. Now he was the host to an ever-changing parade of visitors. "I'd never done that before, so I had to learn quick," he says.

One day as Alii strolled through the garden before heading down to work, he thought about the perennial water shortage in Kula. He realized, "I have to start thinking drought tolerant." Kula's soil is famously fertile. It was the white potatoes grown here that attracted whaling ships to winter off Maui, rather than Oʻahu, and it was the vegetables grown here that fed the California gold miners in 1849 and American troops during World War II. But Kula is also perennially short of rain, and farmers who grow traditional vegetable crops often struggle.

Alii decided it made no sense to plant something that would require a lot of water, and he began researching potential crops. About the same time, he noticed a magazine cover announcing that the International Herb Association had named lavender 1999 Herb of the Year. "I didn't know much about lavender," he recalls. "I didn't even know it was an herb."

And then, in one of the several serendipitous moments that make up the story of Aliʻi Kula Lavender, a friend showed up with a gift: a dried lavender bouquet with a beautiful fragrance. Emma Veary, famed for her lovely voice and her renditions of Hawaiian classics, had been to Oregon, where lavender is plentiful.

"It just grows wild in Oregon," she said.

Alii asked, "You mean like Hana Highway, with all the tropicals?" "No," Emma replied. "The plant was cultivated on farms and even in median strips on the highway."

Lavender farms? Hmmm. To the inveterate gardener, this was an intriguing thought. Alii went down to the local hardware store and asked the clerk if they had any lavender plants. The store had about 20 plants of the French *dentata* variety, and he bought them all and planted them in a row along the driveway. "I wasn't impressed with it," he admits. "I'm used to tropical plants. I didn't have the feeling for this plant," with its gray-green leaves and tiny purple flowers.

But something told him, "Check this out, because it looks like someone is sending a message." And in fact, even though he was gone every day taking care of his vacation rental and gave the lavender little attention, the plant thrived. "It was loving the conditions here," Alii says.

Lavender, it turns out, flourishes in the chronic drought conditions of Kula, which has an average annual rainfall of less than 25 inches. It sips most of the moisture it needs from the mist that often settles over the Kula mountainside in the late afternoon. And lavender likes to bask in full sun on a well-drained, southwest-facing slope—a perfect description of this Kula property. Though native to Europe, its subtle colors look at home on the slopes of Haleakalā. The bugs and animals don't like to nibble on it, and it grows without much attention. This was good, because Alii didn't have time to be fussing with spraying and fertilizing. The colorful and highly valued tropicals are often the target of thieves, but Alii didn't have to worry about that with lavender. "Nobody stole it because they didn't

know what kind of plant it was!" he says. "It was perfect for us. I think the lavender chose me. Lavender won't grow just anywhere. It happens that we're right here under a lucky star."

If "someone" was sending a message, it was coming through loud and clear. This historic plant had found a new home, and this passionate gardener had found a new love. "I came back to the land, and here was lavender, waiting for me to come back," Alii says. "I feel like, in some past life, I was growing lavender! It came natural to me."

In June 2002, Alii sold his Kīhei resort and obtained about 5,000 lavender starts from a propagator in California, then planted them around the existing protea and ornamentals in the area below his house. He began to develop products. The original French dentata, for example, made a great addition to lemonade and scones. Now that he had educated himself about this fascinating plant, it was time to educate the public. The garden began to offer a tour with lemonade, tea and scones.

With an official new name, *Nanea aʻo Kula* (Relaxed in Kula), a new business was underway. "I just thought growing lavender and doing tours was a way to survive," Alii says. "I later found out that what I was doing had a name—it's called agri-tourism. It was more than survival; it was a way to sustain our farm operation."

> *"We are all cups, constantly and quietly being filled. The trick is, knowing how to tip ourselves over and let the beautiful stuff out."*
>
> RAY BRADBURY

In this lovely place, Alii found a way to use all the education and experience he'd gained over the years, from farming and running a business to artistic expression and welcoming visitors from around the world. He had found the perfect focus for his passion.

On The Farm

The next time you're on Maui, be sure to take a little detour and drive Upcountry for an extraordinary experience at the magical lavender gardens on the slopes of Mount Haleakalā. If you are lucky enough to make the trip in April or May, the jacaranda trees will be in bloom, their purple blossoms marking the way to the lavender farm up the hill. Turning off the highway onto a narrow country road with spectacular views, entering the farm's driveway, you might see tiny lavender flags fluttering in even rows across a field, each indicating the location of a new plant. The farm is beautiful and colorful at any time of year, but if you arrive in June, you'll see the mature lavender plants in spectacular purple bloom. Though most varieties of lavender bloom in the spring and summer, in this unique place certain varieties bloom year round.

Even the farm's fields are works of art. "It looks like a garden, but it is a working farm," says Alii, who insists that, even if he planted lettuce, he'd do it in artistic designs.

With the original plantings at the lower end of the property and in the new fields above, thousands of plants flourish.

The farm offers a tea tour and a culinary tour that includes lunch, as well as workshops in which visitors can learn how to weave wreaths out of herbs, lavender, flowers and succulent plants. Guests are also welcome to enjoy daily guided and self-guided tours to view more than 45 different varieties of lavender now growing on the property.

The weather in Kula can change suddenly, and sometimes it concerns visitors who are unfamiliar with the mountain mists that roll down the hillside. Alii reassures them: How often do they have the opportunity to walk in clouds? Visitors usually need not to worry about rain; if it falls, it will be gentle, and umbrellas (purple ones, of course) are waiting in a stand near the shop.

Whether they walk in bright sunshine or amid white clouds that drift down from above, visitors find this garden a place of delight. Paths wind among beds of lavender, each labeled with its variety's common name, and an eclectic collection of other flowering and scented plants. There are potted succulents and ferns, scented geraniums, a spray of orchids in a porcelain pot, enormous iris with purple blooms at eye level and exotic protea in many shapes and colors. Bromeliads and jade plants sprout from a rustic rock wall. Bright yellow nasturtiums twine among blue hydrangeas, and roses climb over a white trellis. Here and there are places to sit and enjoy the view. On one edge of the garden is a grotto under an artistically pruned avocado tree. Its lush greenery and blossoms fill what used to be a *pūnāwai* (cistern), part of a water system used by farmers of generations past. Antique garden ornaments are scattered among the flowers—Chinese lions, bronze cranes, sculpted angels and stone Buddhas.

Just inside the farm's gate, you'll smell the sweet fragrance of the gift shop.

Stone Buddhas, sculpted angels and other statuary decorate the grounds of Ali'i Kula Lavender.

The dragonfly, or pinao, that is the Ali'i Kula Lavender logo was inspired by a real dragonfly that lives around the garden pond. Dragonflies symbolize light, joy, the magic of color and also the transformation we experience as we grow past self-created illusions that limit our growth—all concepts that align with the spirit and philosophy of Ali'i Kula Lavender. Alii Chang remembers seeing many pinao *hovering around the waters of taro patches when he was a child. And everyone joked in those days about "Aunty* Pinao," *a nickname given to women who liked to flit around to social events. In graphic artist Saedene Yee-Ota's vision, the head of Ali'i Kula Lavender's* pinao *is actually a tiny lavender flower.*

Tea, scones, brownies, lavender-lime sorbet and other lavender-flavored food items are available for visitors to enjoy at outdoor tables. Shop shelves are lined with an assortment of products that testifies to lavender's versatility and ability to inspire: chips, syrup, salad dressing, jellies, sunscreen, lotions, soaps, candles, pillow inserts, aprons, pins, pens, flower pots and fabrics.

This amazing array of products all are labeled with the Hawaiian *pinao* (dragonfly), which is the farm's logo. It's not unusual to see one of these delicate creatures flitting about the gardens, and its symbolism—personal rebirth and renewal—is right in line with the philosophy of Ali'i Kula Lavender. This place is a sanctuary from harried modern life. It entices visitors to relax, rejuvenate and renew. ◦§§~

George Allan

CHAPTER TWO

Lavender in the Garden

Y ou may need a few sniffs of lavender to clear your head when you first try to sort out the different varieties of the plant. As one researcher wrote, there is "MUCH confusion, cross-naming, inconsistency in cultivars worldwide." In the various sections, or species, within the genus *Lavandula* there are many subspecies, each of which has a common name (or two) in addition to its Latin botanical name. Each also has a different scent and color, as well as usage. And, different varieties grow better in different areas.

The Ali'i Kula Lavender farm has unique growing conditions, perfect for growing lavender with a stronger scent than other lavender farms elsewhere. The farm's plants also grow rapidly, with the first good crop in less than a year, while farmers in most other places expect to wait until the third year for a really good harvest. The farm also enjoys year-round blooms in several of the varieties it cultivates. The master gardener, Alii, has no explanation for why this should be so, other than the natural conditions of the farm's location. "All I did was follow the rules," he says of his farming technique.

Depending on where you live and whether you have a green thumb like Alii, your experience may not be the same. However, this is a plant so adaptive and loved around the world that you will probably find some variety that will grow for you.

Lavender is a member of the *Labiatae* or mint family, related to thyme, savory, rosemary and sage. A hardy perennial evergreen shrub with a productive life of about 10 years, some of its plants have been known to live for 30 years or more. Lavender's fragrance and medicinal qualities derive from its oils, which differ among the species, and the plant's value depends on the type of oil it produces.

LAVENDER'S 6 SECTIONS

LAVANDULA
- *Also English lavender*
- *Includes angustifolia, lavendins*
- *Ali'i Kula Lavender varieties include Blue Mountain, Victorian Amethyst, Provence, Silver Edge*
- *Hardy, most commonly grown lavenders*

STOECHAS
- *Also Spanish or French lavender*
- *Ali'i Kula Lavender varieties include Otto Quast, Kew Red, White Form*
- *More fragile "tender" lavenders used primarily for landscaping*

DENTATA
- *Also French or fringed lavender*
- *Ali'i Kula Lavender's initial variety*
- *Tender lavender often used in cooking*

PTEROSTOECHAS
- *Also Ferny-leafed lavender*

CHAETOSTACHYS and SUBNUDA
- *Rarely seen in cultivation*

The size and shape of the plant also vary, and flowers can be white, yellow or pink, as well as the more expected blue, mauve or purple.

The genus *Lavandula* is divided into six sections and more than 30 species, which together have produced seemingly enumerable cultivars with a variety of attributes. Ali'i Kula Lavender grows three of those sections—*L. Stoechas, L. Lavandula* and *L. Dentata*. The others are *L. Pterostoechas, L. Chaetostachys* and *L. Subnuda*; the last two sections are rarely seen in cultivation.

Section *Stoechas* (sometimes called Spanish, but sometimes called French) is the lavender of history, the wild plant that the Romans used in their baths and first-aid kits. Today, it is primarily used as a landscape plant. Its fragrance is weak and camphorous, but it has unusual and showy flowers, with wing-like bracts protruding from its square flower head. The bracts are actually leaves, not flower petals. *Stoechas* is one of the "tender" lavenders, which means it will not survive a cold winter—no problem for us in Hawai'i! These tender lavenders may have weaker stems and greener leaves than the hardy types. Aliʻi Kula Lavender grows the cultivars "Otto Quast," "Kew Red," "White Form" and the subspecies *pedunculata*. Some of these plants bloom every four months.

 Section *Lavandula* was once known as *Spica*, a name referring to the plant's spike-like inflorescence. The section's name now is officially *Lavandula* (the same as the genus name), and *Spica* is no longer in use. The plants in this section are the hardiest and most commonly grown lavenders, with many cultivars. Aliʻi Kula Lavender grows several varieties of this "English lavender" and its hybrids, the lavandins. One species is *L. angustifolia*, also known as *L. officianalis, L. vera* and fine lavender. Its delicate fragrance is beloved by perfume makers, and it has been called the "blue gold" of Provence in France. The plants usually have short stems and grow in small, low clumps.

 Among the English lavender varieties Aliʻi Kula grows are "Blue Mountain," "Lady," "Sarah," "Hidcote Purple," "Hidcote Pink," "Victorian Amethyst," "Munstead" and "Jean Davis."

 While some varieties of *L. angustifolia* will grow from seed, plants propagated from seed may be different from the parent plant, so it's usually best to take cuttings.

 The lavandins (*Lavandula x intermedia*) are hybrids, formed by combining *L. angustifolia* with *L. latifolia*, another variety from the *Lavandula* section. *Latifolia* yields three times the oil of *L. angustifolia*, but the oil's high camphor content gives it a medicinal smell. It is used in Spain and Portugal on porcelain and

No matter what variety of lavender you grow, they all need aloha. They cannot grow without it—nothing can. Lavenders need sunlight, like people need praise and recognition to grow. I have names for all my lavender. I call them by name, nurture them, give them attention and loving touch. They respond to me with big, beautiful, fragrant blossoms that bring joy and appreciation to all. Experiencing that really makes me happy. My plants are my babies; when they are sad, so am I.

—Alii Chang

as a thinner for oil paints. This hybrid at first occurred naturally among wild populations due to flower-visiting insects, such as bees. Breeders then purposefully combined *L. latifolia* with the sweet-scented *L. angustifolia* to create a plant with the best of both qualities—high oil quantities and sweet smell. Among the most hardy of all lavenders, these produce long-stemmed flowers commonly used for display and crafts. The flower is good for making sachets.

Ali‘i Kula grows lavandins such as "Grosso," "Provence," "Alba," "Dutch" and "Silver Edge." As hybrids, the lavandins cannot be grown from seed and must be propagated by cuttings.

Lavandins yield between 20 and 95 quarts of oil per acre, compared with *L. angustifolia's* yield of three to 15 quarts of oil per acre, so commercial farmers often focus on lavandin production. On the other hand, the sweet oil of true lavender sells for more than twice as much as that of the lavandins. Lavandins' stronger fragrances, much less subtle than the fine lavender, make them more useful for scenting housecleaning products and detergents.

Section *Dentata* is also known as French lavender or fringed lavender (or sometimes Spanish lavender … see what we mean about the confusion?). The name *dentata* comes from the shape of the plant's leaves—dented or toothed. This tender lavender is the first type Alii Chang planted, the one that showed him the incredible potential for growing this plant in Kula. *Dentata* flowers prolifically through much of the year, but its scent is not as long-lasting as English lavender. Both *dentata* and the English cultivars are used for culinary lavender.

Planting young lavender plants in pots can spare them from unfavorable soil temperatures, plus they can be easily moved to sheltered locations or indoors during cold months.

Growing Your Own

Once you become a lavender lover, it's almost inevitable that you will want to grow some in your own garden. What kind you grow will depend on how you plan to use it, and where you plant it.

"I always look at the natural contour of the land, where water will flow and drain, and I notice the direction of the wind, sun and cloud cover," Alii explains. "Nature is always working together, but you've got to pay attention. I look at the natural gifts of the land and its environment and see the entire field planted in my mind."

Ali'i Kula Lavender is lucky—all those natural gifts add up to the perfect environment for growing lavender, and the image in Alii's mind became reality. May you also find the perfect lavender for your climate and purpose. Here are some tips.

In general, most lavenders prefer hot, dry climates. English lavenders, for instance, grow poorly in the humid southeast, while lavandins can grow as far south as Florida. Being close to a body of water can moderate climate, so even northerly areas can be mild enough for some lavenders. A cover of snow actually helps some plants, such as "Munstead," "Grosso" and "Hidcote," to survive. But most lavenders are susceptible to frost injury, so if you do have severe winters in your area, try to grow your plants in pots and move them to the sunniest possible indoor location for the winter (though most will tolerate a pot only for a year or so before needing to be put into the ground). Or plant them near the windbreak protection of a house or stone wall, and, if necessary, cover them with a bushel basket during the worst weather. Winter is one time when you might want to mulch your lavender with straw or wood chips, but beware of crown rot and bacterial and fungal disease that can result from the mulch holding in too much moisture.

You might also have trouble if you live where there is high summer humidity, because the humidity encourages fungal infection. You will have to be careful to plant in very well-drained soil, avoid overwatering and take special care in drying your harvest.

Perhaps the best way to decide what cultivars will work where you live is to contact local agricultural authorities, such as the county extension service of a state university. Or simply stop by a local plant nursery and see what they carry.

In Hawai'i, growers can plant any time of year.

In mild climates where the seasons are more pronounced than in the Islands, you may plant in the fall, but if you live where winter is harsh, wait for spring. Keep your plant starts outside for a month or so before you put them in the ground, so that they harden off and acclimate to nighttime temperatures.

Lavender grows best in light soil, sand or gravel in dry, open and sunny areas that don't need a lot of fertilizer or irrigation. Good drainage and lots of sun are most important; lavender prefers a warm, very well-

The Estate Lookout at Ali'i Kula Lavender offers an impressive view of upcountry Maui and the wide variety of blossoms and herbs on the property.

drained loam with a slope to the south or southwest. English lavender varieties like chalky soils, whereas the lavandin varieties do better in slightly more acidic soils. Generally, lavender requires a moderately alkaline pH level. If your soil composition is acidic, you may want to use a little lime, well-composted chicken manure and bone meal at planting time. However, in very alkaline soils, these extra ingredients could be too much of a good thing, so have your soil tested and act accordingly.

Plants naturally undergo constant change. Growers can facilitate the process by weeding out old branches, making way for new stems and blossoms.

If your soil has a lot of clay in it, you need to work the soil down at least a foot and a half and add plenty of sand and compost, perhaps raising the bed six inches above ground level. This mound will keep the plant's "feet" dry and allow the drainage necessary to avoid root rot. Placing white sand, gravel, sea shells, oyster shells or marble chips around the base of the plant reflects sun into the interior of the bush and helps keep it dry, reducing problems with fungal infection. A two-inch layer of sand will also help the plant make it through a cold winter.

Lavender can get by with minimal rain—one researcher said 33 inches a year was just right, but Kula averages about 22 inches a year, and the lavender farms of Sequim, Washington, thrive on 16 inches and a couple of supplemental waterings. If your area is really dry and you need to irrigate, do it from below, preferably by the drip method, rather than sprinkling from above. Young plants are more likely to need watering, especially in warm, windy weather. As the plants mature and the roots go deeper, you will need to irrigate and fertilize even less.

Large plants like the lavandins should be spaced about three feet apart, while *L. angustifolia* can get by with about two feet. How far you space them will depend on your purpose. A mass of plants close together and all blooming at once can be spectacular.

A single lavender amid a variety of other flowers in different colors is also beautiful. Keep in mind that large plants, such as the "Grosso," can have a five-foot spread and need plenty of space around them to allow for air circulation.

Lavender can grow in containers, with the small varieties adapting particularly well, but they should be repotted annually in a suitable mixture that includes controlled-release fertilizer. The larger varieties can be planted in very large containers but will need to go into the ground after a couple of years. Be sure to water container plants regularly in the summer. Don't let them dehydrate! Water minimally during the winter months.

Lavender combines beautifully with other plants in a window box or hanging basket. Consider planting lavender in a basket with trailing purple-flowered plants or in a box full of other herbs with healing properties. Remember that container plants need good drainage and full sun, plus more frequent fertilization than those planted in the ground.

Pruning Tips

Plants naturally undergo constant change, and detaching from old branches or bringing forth new stems is all part of a natural process that keeps them growing and vital. Letting go of the excess part of the plant is a plant's way of maintaining balance—in fact, they thrive on detaching from what is useless to their growth.

Harvest early in the day, when the dew is dry but before the sun is too hot.

This is a lesson for people as well. As human beings, we tend to hold onto objects, situations and relationships that no longer give us nourishment. Sometimes holding onto those things drains our vitality, as it does with plants. Detachment is a hard reality for many, but it is often the only way to ensure one's continued growth, happiness and good health.

> *"How fair is a garden amid the trials and passions of existence."*
>
> BENJAMIN DISRAELI

Lavender plants seem to have a particular love for such transformation; they thrive when pruned. You should prune as you go, removing dead leaves and stems as well as fresh flowers to use as they bloom, but your plants will grow best if you also cut them back hard on a regular schedule. To encourage lateral branch growth, nip the shoots when the plants are young and still in the pot. If you prefer bushy and compact plants, clip the buds off plants to prevent flowering the first year. In succeeding years, to maintain the plant's shape and promote new growth, take off as much as half the stem length—just be sure you leave some green leaves on the plant and don't prune deeply into the wood.

Prune early in spring, or in the fall, after most blooming has finished, so you do not delay the next bloom. If you want to propagate new plants, use some of the cuttings you collect in pruning.

When it's time to trim and harvest the plants, cut the lavender stems all the way down to where the foliage begins to show. Cutting the foliage back severely after harvesting results in strong growth in the next season. It ensures that the plant doesn't get too woody, and the next stems will grow straight and tall. If you don't prune the mature blooms and old branches of the lavender, the shrub will have very few blooms the following season.

Weeding is also important, because weeds rob moisture and nutrients from the lavender and increase the humidity around the plant, thus encouraging mildew on its foliage. Laying down a weed-barrier fabric or cultivating carefully by hand will keep weeds away from your lavender. In the same way, it is important for people to remove the "weeds" of negative attitudes, anger, guilt and judgment that rob us of our nutrients and lead to disease. And fortunately, just like people, mature lavender plants are better able to take care of themselves, as their wide-spreading branches shade out the weeds below.

Harvest Time

When you harvest depends on what you plan to do with your crop. Lavender for dried flower purposes should be harvested when the first few florets are open. Flower stalks are cut just under the first pair of leaves. Flowers for oil production and loose blossoms should be harvested when about half of the flowers are blooming. For the best scent, flowers usually are harvested starting in the second year, between the time of early blossom and maximum bloom. Harvest early in the day, when the dew is dry but before the sun is too hot.

To dry your lavender so that it keeps its color and shape in dried arrangements, tie it in bunches with an elastic band. Plant stems shrink during the drying process, and elastic will keep the materials from slipping and falling to the floor. You might want to put them into large brown paper bags, being sure the flowers don't touch the paper, or put a clean sheet or tarp under them to catch any blossoms that fall. With or without a bag, hang the bunches in a dark, warm place with good air circulation. Or you can spread the stems on a cloth-covered screen in a shady, well-ventilated room. They will dry in a few days to a few weeks, depending on the temperature and humidity.

Dry your lavender by tying in bunches and hanging in a dark, warm place with good air circulation.

If you should decide to propagate your own lavender *keiki* (children), do it by cuttings or layering. Though some types of lavender can be grown by seed, chances are they will not breed true to the parent but will be a hybrid, because bees and other insects buzzing between the plants have fertilized the flowers.

To start with a cutting, clip four inches from a disease-free plant in spring when buds are beginning to form (or harvest flowers

For the best scent, lavender is usually harvested between the time of early blossom and maximum bloom.

early, and take your cutting from new growth that appears in late August and early September). Nip any buds and remove all leaves from the bottom half of the cuttings. If you like, you can dip the ends in root hormone. Place them in a well-draining soil medium, perhaps composed of one part perlite and one part peat moss or sand. If you are in a cold climate, you'll have better luck by placing the cuttings on a heat bench for the first month or so of rooting.

You can also propagate lavender by layering. Bend a long, healthy, flexible stem down to the ground and remove a few inches of the foliage, leaving several inches of foliage at the tip. Pile dirt or potting soil over the nodes where you have removed the foliage, with the tip exposed. Use a U-shaped piece of wire or a twig to hold the stem section in place. Keep this rooting section moist, and once it has rooted, cut the new plant from the mother plant and transfer it to a pot.

Growing Lavender, Growing Life

Because lavender needs so little in the way of water and fertilizer and because it does not attract insect pests, it ranks high as a sustainable crop. But because most of the world's essential oil is produced outside the United States, American farmers looking for a commercial crop need to do careful research before plunging into massive lavender plantings. Growers need to be prepared with a marketing plan and a profitable outlet for their crop.

> "Nature always wears the colors of the spirit."
>
> RALPH WALDO EMERSON

If you are contemplating lavender as a commercial crop, study the plant and its potential in depth before taking the plunge. Check the Internet for Web sites posted by professional researchers, such as those at state universities, several of whom have studied commercial lavender production in great detail. Go visit commercial lavender farms to see what they are doing. Or hire a pioneer lavender farmer in your area as a consultant to help you get started. Most experts point out that growing lavender to produce value-added products is the best path to success.

Plants need all the basics to grow: water, sunshine, soil and space. But they really blossom when something more is added to the mix. Gardeners who talk to, touch and care deeply about their plants provide a kind of nutrient that people provide for their dearest friends. ⊙§§~

CHAPTER THREE

Lavender in Your Kitchen

L avender lends a special flavor to many kinds of food and drink. It can be used in stocks, soups, chowders, salads and their dressings, fish, meat and poultry dishes, desserts, baked goods, jams, jellies, syrups, vinegars, pickles, chutneys, and ketchups, and in drinks from tea to lemonade to margaritas. Its use extends back to ancient times, but modern lavender lovers are constantly coming up with new ways to use the herb.

The sweet angustifolias are great for culinary use, as is dentata, but the more camphorous varieties should be avoided. Use only a small amount of lavender to flavor food; too much can be overwhelming. Be sure that any lavender added to food is organically grown and has not been sprayed with pesticides.

Over the years, Ali'i Kula Lavender chefs and partners have come up with many fabulous lavender-inspired recipes, many of which are shared in this chapter. (Sorry, you won't find the formula for the farm's famous lavender lemonade here. It's a family secret!) However, to make cooking with lavender easy, the farm developed several pre-made mixes, seasonings and dressings. (The farm's products are capitalized in the recipes.) In this chapter, you'll find more than 35 recipes to try, from a Lavender Crab & Mango Spring Rolls appetizer to a Pound Cake with Blueberries & Lavender Syrup dessert. Enjoy!

LAVENDER CRAB & MANGO SPRING ROLLS
by Chef Paul Lamparelli of Dr. Fedwell Catering

Serves 6 to 8

SPRING ROLLS:

1 c.	BLUE CRAB MEAT, COOKED
½ c.	FRESH MANGO, DICED
	PINCH OF CULINARY LAVENDER FLOWERS
1 Tbsp.	LAVENDER GOURMET SEASONING
1	CUCUMBER, JULIENNED
1	LARGE CARROT, JULIENNED
4 oz.	RADISH SPROUTS
1 pkg.	THAI RICE PAPER SPRING ROLL WRAPPERS (ROUND)

In a large bowl, mix crab with mango and seasonings. Divide mixture into six portions. Lay down a clean linen napkin on your counter or cutting board. Make spring rolls one at a time. Pour warm water in a wide-rim, shallow bowl or plate. Dredge rice paper through warm water for a few seconds, but not until soft. Lay wrapper down on linen napkin and add one portion of the crab mix. Cover with layers of the vegetables and roll bottom up. Bring in sides and roll all the way up.

DIPPING SAUCE:

1 Tbsp.	LAVENDER LILIKOʻI JELLY
1 Tbsp.	LAVENDER HERB VINEGAR
1 Tbsp.	WATER
	FRESH GROUND PEPPER, TO TASTE

Mix together for dipping sauce.

Lavender Scallops

by Chef Paul Lamparelli

Serves 6

2	MEDIUM GOLD POTATOES, BOILED AND COOLED
3 Tbsp.	OLIVE OIL
	LAVENDER GOURMET SEASONING
2	GARLIC CLOVES, MINCED
2 c.	FRESH SPINACH LEAVES
	LAVENDER PEPPER SEASONING
6	LARGE SEA SCALLOPS
1	LEMON, WEDGE
1 TSP.	BUTTER

Trim ends and slice potatoes in ½-inch-thick pieces. Heat large sauté pan over medium-high flame. Pour 2 Tbsp. olive oil into pan, add potato slices and sprinkle with Lavender Gourmet Seasoning. Cook potatoes until crisp on both sides. Remove and arrange at least six pieces on a plate. While pan is still hot, add 1 Tbsp. olive oil and minced garlic. As soon as garlic sizzles, add spinach leaves and a pinch of Lavender Gourmet Seasoning. Stir until spinach is wilted. Mound equal parts of spinach over individual potato slices.

Sprinkle Lavender Pepper Seasoning over scallops. Heat sauté pan again and add oil when hot. Sear scallops on both sides. Place one scallop on top of each potato-spinach mound, and return pan to heat. Squeeze lemon into pan with scallop juices and reduce a few moments. Whisk in butter to complete sauce and pour over scallops.

OPAH APPETIZER
by Chef Julia

Serves 8 to 10

¼ C.	ORGANIC OLIVE OIL
1	PIECE FRESH OPAH (MOONFISH)
1 TSP.	CULINARY LAVENDER
2	BUNCHES ORGANIC BELGIUM ENDIVE
	LAVENDER LILIKOʻI JELLY

Drizzle oil over fish and sprinkle Culinary Lavender on top. Grill fish for 7 to 10 minutes on a medium heat. Slice endive lengthwise and fashion together into a nice display. Lay opah on top. Garnish with one spoon of Lavender Lilikoʻi Jelly and a dried or fresh lavender flower.

LAVENDER CHICKEN & FETA MEATBALLS

by Chef Paul Lamparelli

Serves 8 to 10

MEATBALLS:

1 LB.	CHICKEN BREAST, GROUND
1 TBSP.	PARSLEY, CHOPPED
1 TBSP.	CHIVES, CHOPPED
1 TSP.	SALT
2 TBSP.	KALAMATA OLIVES, CHOPPED
	LAVENDER PEPPER SEASONING
2	WHOLE EGGS
⅔ C.	CRUMBLED FETA CHEESE
	BREADCRUMBS

Mix chicken with herbs, salt, olives and freshly ground Lavender Pepper Seasoning. When mixed well, add eggs, cheese, and enough breadcrumbs to make a stiff mixture. Roll into 1-inch balls, and place on parchment-lined baking sheet. Bake in 350°F oven until cooked through. Serve with lavender-mint yogurt.

LAVENDER-MINT YOGURT:

1 C.	LOW-FAT YOGURT
1 TBSP.	LAVENDER HERB VINEGAR
½ TSP.	SALT
1 TBSP.	MINT LEAVES, CHOPPED
	LAVENDER PEPPER SEASONING, FRESHLY CRACKED

Whisk all ingredients together and chill.

LAVENDER-HERB BEEF WON TON

by Chef Crystal Carroll

Serves 2 to 4

1 LB.	GROUND BEEF
1	EGG
1 C.	KULA (OR ROUND) ONION, DICED
1-2 TBSP.	LAVENDER GOURMET SEASONING
1 TBSP.	SOY SAUCE
	DASH OF SALT AND PEPPER
1 PKG.	WON TON PI WRAPPERS
	VEGETABLE OIL

In a large bowl, combine ground beef, egg, onion, Lavender Gourmet Seasoning, soy sauce, salt and pepper. Wrap 1 Tbsp. of beef mixture in won ton pi wrapper. Close ends of won ton pi wrapper by dipping finger tips in water and running along edges to seal the bottom edge to the top edge. Fry in 1-inch of oil over medium heat until won ton is crispy.

LAVENDER PEPPERED 'AHI SASHIMI WITH ASIAN PEAR RELISH

by Chef Paul Lamparelli

Serves 2 to 4

'AHI SASHIMI:

2 TBSP.	LAVENDER PEPPER SEASONING
1 TBSP.	LAVENDER GOURMET SEASONING
6-8 OZ.	YELLOWFIN TUNA SASHIMI BLOCK
	OLIVE OIL

In a wide-rim, shallow bowl, mix together Lavender Pepper Seasoning with Lavender Gourmet Seasoning. Roll the fish in the mixture. Sear in a hot pan with olive oil for 30 seconds on each side. Chill for 10 minutes.

ASIAN PEAR RELISH:

1	ASIAN PEAR, CORED AND QUARTERED
2 TBSP.	OLIVE OIL
	PINCH OF LAVENDER GOURMET SEASONING
¼ C.	SWEET RED PEPPER, FINELY DICED
¼ C.	SWEET KULA ONION, FINELY DICED
1 TBSP.	CHIVES, MINCED
1 TBSP.	LAVENDER HERB VINEGAR

Rub pear sections with some of olive oil and a pinch of Lavender Gourmet Seasoning.

Combine remaining ingredients. You may chop the pears and add them to the relish or serve them separately in quarters. Dip sashimi into relish.

LAVENDER GRAVLAX

by Chef Paul Lamparelli

Serves 8 to 10
Prep time: 24 hours
Start this preparation 2 to 3 days before serving.

1 LB.	2 SALMON FILLETS (WITH SKIN, BUT PINBONES REMOVED)
	LAVENDER GOURMET SEASONING
1 LEMON	ZEST
2 OZ.	COGNAC OR BRANDY

Cover work area with several sheets of plastic wrap interwoven to make a large sheet a few layers thick. Lay both fillets skin side down. Pat dry and rub generously with Lavender Gourmet Seasoning. All flesh should be covered. Sprinkle lemon zest equally over the tops. Pour cognac or brandy along the center of each fillet. Place one fillet on top of the other with the flesh (seasoned sides) facing each other. Wrap salmon very tightly and place in baking dish in refrigerator. Place an equal size dish on top of salmon and weight down with a bowl of water or a few cans of food. Allow salmon to cure for at least 24 hours, but a little longer is better.

Remove the fish from the plastic and wipe away seasonings. Rinse in cold water and pat dry. If using whole fillets, remove 1 or 2 inches of meat from the tail and taste test. With a long, sharp knife, thinly slice the remaining fish. Serve with favorite breads, relishes, pickles, etc.

LAVENDER SHRIMP WITH SWEET-CHILI DIPPING SAUCE

by Chefs Matt and Glenn

Serves 4

SWEET-CHILI DIPPING SAUCE:

2 TBSP.	SAMBAL THAI CHILI PASTE
3 TBSP.	HONEY
1/4 C.	LAVENDER VINEGAR
1/4 C.	PEANUT OIL (SUBSTITUTE WITH OLIVE OIL IF NEEDED)

In a medium-size bowl, mix chili paste, honey, vinegar and oil.

LAVENDER SHRIMP:

1 LB.	16 TO 20 SHRIMP, RAW
2 TBSP.	LAVENDER GOURMET SEASONING
	OLIVE OIL TO COAT SHRIMP

In a large bowl, mix shrimp with Lavender Gourmet Seasoning and coat with olive oil. In a large sauté pan, cook shrimp for approximately 5 minutes. Place a small ramekin of dipping sauce in the middle of a platter. Arrange shrimp around the edges of the plate.

LAVENDER LENTIL SALAD

by Chef Paul Lamparelli

Serves 8

1 c.	DRY GREEN LENTILS
3 c.	CHICKEN STOCK OR WATER
1 Tbsp.	LAVENDER GOURMET SEASONING
1	GARLIC CLOVE, CRUSHED
1	MEDIUM TOMATO, DICED
1	CELERY STALK, FINELY DICED
2	SCALLIONS, FINELY SLICED
½	CUCUMBER, SEEDED AND DICED
2 Tbsp.	PARSLEY, CHOPPED
½ c.	LAVENDER HERB DRESSING

Rinse and drain lentils. Bring lentils, stock, Lavender Gourmet Seasoning and garlic to a simmer. Lower heat and cook covered until tender. Drain and cool. Mix with remaining ingredients and chill for 30 minutes.

LAVENDER-HERB CHICKEN SALAD

by Chefs Matt and Glenn

Serves 8

LAVENDER-HERB CHICKEN:

3	BONELESS CHICKEN BREASTS
	LAVENDER GOURMET SEASONING

Rub chicken with Lavender Gourmet Seasoning. Bake at 400°F for 15 to 20 minutes. Let cool, and then cut into strips.

SALAD:

¼ HEAD	WON BOK CHINESE CABBAGE, ROUGHLY CHOPPED
⅛ HEAD	RED CABBAGE, FINELY SLICED
½	RED BELL PEPPER, DICED
½	YELLOW BELL PEPPER, DICED
½	ORANGE BELL PEPPER, DICED
1	SMALL CARROT, JULIENNED
	WON TON STRIPS, FOR GARNISH
	ORGANIC KULA GREENS OR OTHER SALAD GREENS
	LAVENDER HERB DRESSING, TO TASTE

Toss all salad ingredients together. Pour Lavender Herb Dressing over the salad and toss right before serving. Place seasoned chicken strips over salad and serve.

Warm Lavender Potato Salad

by Chefs Matt and Glenn

Serves 6

4	LARGE RUSSET BAKING POTATOES, PEELED AND DICED
1½ TBSP.	DIJON MUSTARD
2	LARGE SHALLOTS, MINCED
1 BUNCH	CHIVES, CHOPPED
2 TBSP.	MAYONNAISE
2 TBSP.	LAVENDER HERB VINEGAR
	SALT AND PEPPER TO TASTE

Boil potatoes in a large pot until tender. In a large bowl, mix the remaining ingredients. Drain potatoes and fold them into the mayonnaise mixture. Season to taste.

Lavender Cauliflower Vichyssoise

by Chef Paul Lamparelli

Serves 8 to 10

2	LARGE RUSSET POTATOES, PEELED AND CUBED
1	LARGE LEEK, CUT INTO 1-INCH SECTIONS
1	SMALL HEAD CAULIFLOWER, CHOPPED
2 QTS.	CHICKEN STOCK
1 TBSP.	CULINARY LAVENDER
2	GARLIC CLOVES, CRUSHED
2 TBSP.	OLIVE OIL
2½ TBSP.	SALT
2 TSP.	WHITE PEPPER
	CHIVES, FOR GARNISH

Peel and cut potatoes into 1-inch cubes and cover them with water. Clean leek and chop into 1-inch sections, including all of the white and some of the pale-green part. Chop cauliflower into small florets. Heat chicken stock on back burner to just a simmer and add Culinary Lavender. Keep stock at just a simmer. In a 4 qt. pot, sauté leeks and garlic with olive oil over medium flame until soft. Add cauliflower and sauté until it sweats. Add simmering stock to vegetables, straining out lavender as you pour. When soup has returned to a simmer, drain potatoes and add to soup. Add all seasonings and cook until potatoes are tender. Allow soup to cool for 10 minutes. In a blender, purée soup in batches and pour together in a large pot. Chill and serve garnished with fresh chives, freshly shucked oysters or a spoonful of caviar.

Frisée Fruit Salad with Maui Lavender Dressing

Serves 10

20 OZ.	FRISÉE LETTUCE
5 OZ.	GREEN GRAPES, CUT IN HALF
4	GRANNY OR OTHER TART APPLES, SLICED
	JUICE OF ONE LEMON
10 OZ.	LAVENDER HERB DRESSING
½ C.	WALNUTS, CHOPPED
5 OZ.	BLUE CHEESE, CRUMBLED

Rinse and dry frisée lettuce and chill till ready to serve. Rinse grapes well and cut in half. Slice apples and preserve with lemon juice and chill. When ready to serve, toss the lettuce with Maui Lavender Dressing. Top with apple slices, grapes, walnuts, blue cheese. Serve on a chilled plate.

LAVENDER FOCACCIA

by Chef Paul Lamparelli

Serves 8

1 TBSP.	SUGAR OR HONEY
1⅔ C.	WATER, DIVIDED
1 PACKET	DRIED YEAST
5 C.	BREAD FLOUR
6 TBSP.	OLIVE OIL, DIVIDED
2 TSP.	SALT
1 TBSP.	CULINARY LAVENDER, FINELY CHOPPED
2	GARLIC CLOVES, MINCED
1 TSP.	COARSE SEA SALT
¼ TSP.	BLACK PEPPER

In a small bowl, combine sugar or honey with ½ c. of warm water. Sprinkle yeast over the mixture; let the mixture stand until foamy, 5 to 8 minutes.

Sift the bread flour into a large bowl. Make a well in the center of the flour and pour in remaining water, yeast mixture and 4 Tbsp. olive oil. Mix approximately 5 minutes or until a dough is formed; transfer to your work surface. Knead for 10 minutes, then add the salt and knead for approximately 6 to 10 minutes or until the dough is very smooth (if the dough sticks to your hands, add some additional flour, 1 Tbsp. at a time).

Spray a large bowl with nonstick cooking spray. Form the dough into a ball and place dough in the bowl. Cover with plastic wrap, and set aside in a warm place (draft free) to rise for approximately 45 to 60 minutes, or until dough has doubled in bulk.

Preheat oven to 400°F. Lightly oil a large baking sheet. Lightly flour work surface and roll out dough into a large rectangle. Transfer dough to the baking sheet, cover with plastic wrap and let rise approximately 30 to 45 minutes or until it doubles in size.

While dough is rising, make the lavender garlic topping. Finely chop the lavender. In a small bowl, mix lavender and garlic with the remaining 2 Tbsp. of olive oil. Make dimples in the dough with your fingers by pushing into the dough several times. Brush the lavender-garlic topping all over and into the dimples. Sprinkle coarse salt and pepper on top. Bake for 30 to 35 minutes or until golden brown.

PECAN-PEPPER GOAT CHEESE WITH TRUFFLE HONEY & TOMATOES

by Chef Paul Lamparelli

Serves 4

PECAN-PEPPER GOAT CHEESE:

½ LB.	GOAT CHEESE, DIVIDED IN 4
½ C.	PECANS OR MACADAMIA NUTS, FINELY CHOPPED
¼ C.	LAVENDER PEPPER SEASONING
	PINCH OF LAVENDER GOURMET SEASONING
	OLIVE OIL TO COOK

Roll 4 chunks of goat cheese into balls so that they are smooth, then flatten into discs. In a medium bowl, mix nuts and seasonings. Press seasoning mixture into the cheese discs until they are well coated. Chill for one hour or freeze for 10 minutes. Heat nonstick pan and add 2 Tbsp. olive oil. Sauté both sides until crisp.

TOMATO SALAD:

2	MEDIUM VINE RIPE TOMATOES, WEDGES
	PINCH OF CULINARY LAVENDER
	PINCH OF LAVENDER GOURMET SEASONING
1 TBSP.	LAVENDER HERB VINEGAR
1 TBSP.	OLIVE OIL

Toss all ingredients together while you wait for the cheese to chill.

TRUFFLE HONEY SAUCE:

2 TBSP.	LAVENDER HONEY
2 TBSP.	WHITE TRUFFLE OIL

Stir together ingredients and spoon over crispy goat cheese. Serve with tomato salad.

LAVENDER AU GRATIN

Serves 4 to 6

2 TBSP.	BUTTER
6	MEDIUM RUSSET BAKING POTATOES
1 TBSP.	GARLIC
	PINCH OF NUTMEG
	PINCH OF LAVENDER GOURMET SEASONING
	SALT AND PEPPER, TO TASTE
1 ½ C.	HEAVY CREAM

Preheat oven to 400°F. In a casserole dish, spread butter to cover the entire bottom of the dish. Peel and thinly slice potatoes and sprinkle with garlic, a pinch of nutmeg, Lavender Gourmet Seasoning, and salt and pepper to taste. Cover the top with heavy cream. Bake for 30 minutes.

Lavender Bruschetta
by Chefs Matt and Glenn

Serves 4 to 6

1	FRENCH BREAD LOAF, SLICED
	OLIVE OIL TO COOK
2	WHITE ONIONS
	LAVENDER VINEGAR
3	FRESH TOMATOES, CUBED
	DASH LAVENDER GOURMET SEASONING

Heat sliced bread in oven at 375°F until golden brown. Brush with olive oil. In a sauté pan with olive oil, cook white onions until they are caramelized. Deglaze with lavender vinegar. Toss in cubed tomatoes. Add a dash of Lavender Gourmet Seasoning. Pour over hot bread.

LAVENDER-PEPPER POLENTA WITH WARM TOMATO VINAIGRETTE

by Chef Paul Lamparelli

Serves 8 to 10

WARM TOMATO VINAIGRETTE:

1	LARGE TOMATO, CORED AND QUARTERED
¼	SWEET ONION, SLICED THICK
1	GARLIC CLOVE, CRUSHED
	SALT AND PEPPER, TO TASTE
¼ C.	LAVENDER HERB VINEGAR
1 TSP.	FRESH THYME LEAVES
2	WHOLE BASIL LEAVES
½ C.	OLIVE OIL

Preheat oven to 450°F. In a small baking or roasting dish, combine tomato, onion and garlic. Drizzle with a little olive oil and sprinkle generously with salt and pepper. Toss this mixture until it is coated well. Roast until tomatoes are soft and garlic and onions are brown. Onion may be a little toasted on the edges. Deglaze pan with some of the vinegar and transfer contents to a blender. Add remaining vinegar and herbs. Blend on a low speed. Slowly drizzle in olive oil until sauce is thick.

LAVENDER-PEPPER POLENTA:

4 C.	CHICKEN STOCK OR MILK
1 ½ TBSP.	SALT
1 TBSP.	LAVENDER PEPPER SEASONING
1 C.	FINE CORNMEAL
2 TBSP.	PARSLEY, CHOPPED
½ C.	PARMESAN CHEESE, GRATED
	OLIVE OIL

Bring stock to a simmer and add salt and Lavender Pepper Seasoning. Slowly whisk in the cornmeal to the simmering stock; there should be no lumps. Lower heat to medium and continue to stir with a wooden spoon. It needs to be stirred fairly often for 10 to 15 minutes. When polenta is quite thick and pulls away from the sides of the pot, fold in parsley and cheese. Pour into 8" x 8" baking dish. Cover with plastic wrap and smooth surface by pressing down with a same-sized pan. Chill completely. Polenta can than be cut into any shape desired. It may be seared on top and bottom in a nonstick pan with minimal oil, or deep fried for an even crispier taste.

LAVENDER GOAT CHEESE SCALLOPED POTATOES
by Chef Paul Lamparelli

Serves 8 to 10

SALADS & SIDES

1 C.	HEAVY CREAM
1 TSP.	CULINARY LAVENDER
8 OZ.	CHÈVRE (SOFT GOAT CHEESE)
1 TBSP.	SALT
	LAVENDER PEPPER SEASONING, FRESHLY GROUND
1 TSP.	BUTTER
2	LARGE RUSSET POTATOES

In a small saucepan, bring cream almost to a simmer and remove from heat. Crumble lavender flowers with fingers and sprinkle into cream. Add goat cheese, salt and a few grinds of Lavender Pepper Seasoning; whisk. Butter an 8" x 8" baking dish. Peel potatoes and slice in to a uniform thickness using a food processor or any flat slicing blade, such as the one on a box grater. In an overlapping pattern, layer the potato slices in the buttered pan. Pour the cheese mixture over potatoes and cover with foil. Bake for 1 hour at 350°F, removing the foil during the last 10 minutes.

LAVENDER HERB BAKED CHICKEN

by Chefs Matt and Glenn

Serves 2

1 PKG.	CHICKEN BREASTS OR THIGHS
	LAVENDER GOURMET SEASONING
	BUTTER

Place chicken on foil-covered cooking pan. Sprinkle with Lavender Gourmet Seasoning. Place a pat of butter on each piece of chicken. Bake at 350°F for 35 minutes.

LAVENDER-LILIKO'I CHICKEN

by Chef Crystal Carroll

Serves: 4

LAVENDER- LILIKO'I CHICKEN:

1-2 LB.	BONELESS, SKINLESS CHICKEN THIGHS
½ C.	LAVENDER HERB DRESSING
1 ½ TBSP.	LAVENDER GOURMET SEASONING

In a medium bowl, combine chicken thighs, Lavender Herb Dressing and Lavender Gourmet Seasoning; mix well. Chicken may be cut into strips if desired. Cook over medium heat until done. Also great when cooked on a barbecue grill.

LILIKO'I SAUCE:

¼ C.	SOY SAUCE
¼ C.	LAVENDER SUGAR
2 ½ TBSP.	LAVENDER LILIKO'I JELLY

In a medium saucepan over medium heat, sauté soy sauce, sugar and jelly, stirring until sauce gets thick. Pour over chicken and serve with rice or potatoes. Excellent over salad greens too!

LAVENDER SEARED ‘AHI WITH NAMASU

by Chef Paul Lamparelli

Serves 2 to 4

NAMASU:

	SALT
1	CUCUMBER, THINLY SLICED (PREFERABLY JAPANESE OR BURPLESS)
½	CARROT, FINE JULIENNED
2	SCALLIONS, CHOPPED
½ C.	LAVENDER HERB VINEGAR
1 TBSP.	LAVENDER HONEY
2 TBSP.	LAVENDER GOURMET SEASONING

Salt cucumbers and set aside for 30 minutes. When cucumbers are limp, drain away salty water. Add vegetables, vinegar, honey and a pinch of salt. Mix and refrigerate.

LAVENDER SEARED ‘AHI:

1 TBSP.	LAVENDER PEPPER SEASONING
4-6 OZ.	‘AHI TUNA SASHIMI BLOCK
2 TBSP.	VEGETABLE OIL

On a plate, combine Gourmet Seasoning and Pepper Seasoning. Roll tuna block in spices until well coated. Heat a sauté pan over medium high heat. When ready, add 2 Tbsp. oil to pan and add ‘ahi. Cook for 30 seconds on each side, adding more oil if necessary. Try to cook approximately one-quarter of an inch on all sides. Place fish on a paper-towel-lined plate and chill for 10 minutes. With a sharp knife, slice fish and serve with Namasu.

Lavender Eggs Benedict

by Chef Crystal Carroll

Serves 4

4 Tbsp.	olive oil
2 Tbsp.	Lavender Gourmet Seasoning
1 lb.	boneless, skinless chicken thighs, thinly sliced
	Pepper, to taste
8	English muffins, toasted
8	eggs
2 pkgs.	Knorr Special Hollandaise Sauce

In a bowl, combine olive oil and Lavender Gourmet Seasoning. Add in chicken along with pepper. Mix slightly. Over medium heat, fry chicken until cooked all the way through.

Prepare hollandaise sauce as instructed on the package. Fry or poach eggs to your desire. Toast muffins to your liking.

Place toasted English muffin halves on a plate, then place a chicken fillet on each muffin and an egg over chicken fillet. Drizzle hollandaise sauce over each muffin.

Lavender Seared Duck with Plum Wine Sauce

by Chef Paul Lamparelli

Serves 2 to 4

	HALF-BOTTLE OF JAPANESE PLUM WINE
3 SLICES	FRESH GINGER
1	GARLIC CLOVE
	PINCH OF CULINARY LAVENDER
2	DUCK BREASTS, ABOUT 6 OZ. EACH
	SPRINKLE OF LAVENDER GOURMET SEASONING
1 TSP.	DIJON MUSTARD
1 TBSP.	BUTTER
¼ TSP.	WHITE PEPPER
	SALT

Begin simmering plum wine with ginger, garlic and a good pinch of Culinary Lavender. Slowly reduce until wine is one-quarter the original volume. While reducing, score skin sides of duck with a sharp knife. Heat oven to 350°F. Sprinkle Lavender Gourmet Seasoning over skin side of duck and place skin down in an oven-proof sauté pan. Sprinkle the other side with more Lavender Gourmet Seasoning. As the duck sears, pour a little of the duck fat out of the pan. Do not turn duck over until skin side is brown and crisp. Sear other side for 1 minute and transfer to oven for 5 minutes. Remove duck and set on board to rest. Return pan to heat, and deglaze with strained wine reduction. Reduce liquids until glossy and somewhat thick. Thicken with mustard and butter. Season with white pepper and salt, if necessary. Slice breasts and serve with sauce.

Lavender Glazed Ham

Serves 9

3 LB.	HAM
2 C.	LAVENDER SUGAR
1 C.	MUSTARD
5 TO 6	PINEAPPLE SLICES
	CLOVES

Preheat oven to 300°F. Score ham and place in baking pan. Insert cloves into ham. In a separate bowl, mix sugar and mustard together. Brush mixture onto ham and coat generously. Place pineapple slices on ham, cover with foil and place in oven. Bake for 40 minutes. Uncover ham and turn oven off. Let sit for 15 minutes. Slice to desired thickness and serve. Delicious with sweet potatoes on the side.

Lavender Mahimahi
with Lavender-Liliko'i Glaze

by Chef Glenn Carpenter

Serves 4 to 6

Lavender Mahimahi:

6	MAHIMAHI FILLETS
	LAVENDER GOURMET SEASONING
	FLOUR FOR DREDGING
1 PKG.	PANKO (JAPANESE BREADCRUMBS)
2	EGGS, MIXED WITH ¾ C. MILK
	OLIVE OIL

Season fillets with Lavender Gourmet Seasoning. Dredge the fillets in flour (shake off excess), then dip into egg mixture (let excess drip off) and roll in panko. Pan-fry fillets in olive oil until golden brown on each side.

Lavender-Liliko'i Glaze:

1	SMALL MAUI ONION, DICED
1 TBSP.	GINGER, MINCED
	OLIVE OIL
1 TSP.	SAMBAL (GARLIC-CHILI PASTE)
1 CAN	CHICKEN STOCK
3 TBSP.	LAVENDER LILIKO'I JELLY
2 TBSP.	CORNSTARCH, MIXED WITH 3 TBSP. WATER

Sauté onion and ginger with olive oil until soft. Add Sambal, chicken stock and Lavender Liliko'i Jelly; bring to a simmer. Add cornstarch mixture to thicken. Pour mixture over fillets and serve on a bed of salad greens or rice.

ENTRÉES

LAVENDER CRAB CAKES
by Glenn Carpenter

Serves 2

CRAB CAKES:

1	16-OZ. CAN CRAB MEAT
1	EGG
3 TBSP.	MAYONNAISE
3 TBSP.	LAVENDER GOURMET SEASONING
½	RED BELL PEPPER, FINELY DICED
½	YELLOW BELL PEPPER, FINELY DICED
1 ¾ C.	PANKO FLAKES (JAPANESE BREADCRUMBS)

Reserve 1 c. of the panko flakes. Mix remaining ingredients until combined. Form mixture into small cakes (about 3 inches round by ½-inch wide) and roll in the reserved panko. Fry the crab cakes in olive oil for approximately 2 to 3 minutes on each side, or until light brown.

DRESSING:

½ TBSP.	SAMBAL (GARLIC-CHILI PASTE)
3 TBSP.	LAVENDER HONEY
3 TBSP.	CULINARY LAVENDER
¼ C.	VINEGAR
½ C.	OLIVE OIL

Combine all ingredients, except the olive oil. Slowly mix in the olive oil until it is completely incorporated.

ENTRÉES

RELISH:

2	MANGOES, DICED
½	RED ONION, MINCED
¼ C.	LAVENDER VINEGAR
	SALT, TO TASTE

Mix all ingredients until combined.

To serve:
Arrange the cooked crab cakes on a platter, drizzle with the dressing and then place 1 Tbsp. of relish on top of each cake.

ENTRÉES

Lavender Pistachio Lamb Chops
by Chef Paul Lamparelli

Serves 8

⅔ c.	PISTACHIOS, TOASTED
2 TBSP.	CULINARY LAVENDER
8	LAMB CHOPS (OR A RACK OF LAMB)
	SALT AND PEPPER, TO TASTE
	OLIVE OIL
½ c.	HONEY

Preheat oven to 400°F. In a food processor pulse the pistachios and lavender until all nuts are broken up but not powdered. Season lamb with salt and pepper. Heat a heavy-gauge or cast-iron pan to medium-high heat. Add enough oil to coat the pan well. Add chops and sear well, turning once. Set aside.

In a small saucepan, gently warm honey. Dredge each chop in honey, then in lavender/pistachio mixture. Place on sheet pan and finish cooking in oven for 10 to 12 minutes. Let rest 5 minutes for chops or 10 minutes for rack before carving.

Lavender Skewered Shrimp
by Chef Paul Lamparelli

Serves 4

LAVENDER SKEWERED SHRIMP:

4	LARGE, LONG AND FIRM STALKS OF FRESH LAVENDER
12	SHRIMP
	OLIVE OIL
	LAVENDER PEPPER SEASONING

Use large, long and firm stalks of fresh lavender to skewer three large shrimp on each stalk. Coat shrimp with a little olive oil and grind Lavender Pepper Seasoning. Grill on high flame and serve with favorite relish, or try the cucumber relish recipe below.

CUCUMBER RELISH:

1 c.	CUCUMBER, DICED
¼ c.	SWEET RED PEPPER, FINELY DICED
¼ c.	KULA ONION, FINELY DICED
¼ c.	CAPERS, CHOPPED
1 Tbsp.	SMOOTH DIJON MUSTARD
1 Tbsp.	LAVENDER HERB VINEGAR
2 tsp.	LAVENDER GOURMET SEASONING

Combine all ingredients; mix well.

Lavender Gourmet Seasoning Crusted Liliko'i Shrimp

by Chef Crystal Carroll

Serves 3

12	RAW SHRIMP, WASHED, SHELLED AND DE-VEINED
	LAVENDER GOURMET SEASONING
1 TBSP.	CANOLA OR OLIVE OIL
3 TBSP.	LAVENDER LILIKO'I JELLY
¼ HEAD	CABBAGE (A MIX OF CHINESE, RED AND REGULAR CABBAGE IS BEST)
	LAVENDER HERB DRESSING

Marinate shrimp with Lavender Gourmet Seasoning for 15 minutes or more. Cook shrimp in oil on medium-high heat until shrimp turns pink. Add Lavender Liliko'i Jelly directly into pan and cook along with shrimp.

To complete the presentation, finely cut cabbage and mix with Lavender Herb Dressing. Place on a plate and top with shrimp. Makes a delicious appetizer too!

Oven Baked Mahimahi with Maui Lavender Gourmet Seasoning

Serves 5

MAHIMAHI:

| 5 | 7 OZ. MAHIMAHI FILLETS |
| | LAVENDER GOURMET SEASONING |

Preheat oven to 325°F. Sparingly coat fish filets with Lavender Gourmet Seasoning. Place fish in baking pan and cover with foil. Place pan in oven and bake for 30 minutes.

WHITE SAUCE:

2½ C.	BUTTER
5 C.	HEAVY CREAM
5 TSP.	CHOPPED GARLIC
2½ C.	WHITE WINE
	SALT AND PEPPER, TO TASTE
	LEMON WEDGES, FOR GARNISH
	PARSLEY, FOR GARNISH

In a saucepan, combine white sauce ingredients and cook over low heat until sauce is reduced. Pour white sauce over fish before serving. Garnish with lemon wedges and parsley. Serve with steamed rice and sautéed vegetables.

Lavender Shrimp Scampi on Pasta
by Chef Crystal Carroll

Serves 4

1 C.	BUTTER, CUBED, DIVIDED
1	GARLIC CLOVE, MINCED
1-2 TSP.	LAVENDER GOURMET SEASONING
1	KULA (OR ROUND) ONION, DICED
1	MEDIUM-SIZE TOMATO, DICED
1 LB.	RAW SHRIMP, WASHED, PEELED AND DE-VEINED
1 PKG.	SPAGHETTI NOODLES OR ANGEL HAIR PASTA

In medium saucepan over medium-high heat, melt ½ c. of butter, adding in garlic and Lavender Gourmet Seasoning. Add in onions and sauté until almost tender. Add remaining butter and tomatoes. When tomatoes are tender, add shrimp and turn to low heat to simmer. Cook for 2 to 5 minutes or until shrimp turns pink. Remove from heat. Serve over cooked pasta.

LAVENDER-GRILLED PORK TENDERLOIN WITH PLUM CHUTNEY

by Chef Paul Lamparelli

Serves 4 to 6

PLUM CHUTNEY:

4	WHOLE PLUMS
1 TBSP.	GINGER, MINCED
½	SWEET ONION, DICED
½	SWEET RED PEPPER, DICED
½ TSP.	CAYENNE PEPPER
½ TSP.	SALT
½ C.	LAVENDER HERB VINEGAR
¼ C.	SUGAR

Remove pits from plums and cut each plum into eight pieces. Add all remaining ingredients to a non-reactive saucepan. Cook over medium heat until soft. Pour into dish and chill.

LAVENDER- GRILLED PORK:

1	1 ½ LB. WHOLE PORK TENDERLOIN
	LAVENDER GOURMET SEASONING
	OLIVE OIL

Rub the outside of pork tenderloin with Lavender Gourmet Seasoning and a bit of olive oil. Grill over medium-high heat until desired doneness. Allow to rest 10 minutes after grilling before slicing. Serve with Plum Chutney.

LAVENDER PEPPER-SPICED SHRIMP WITH GRILLED CORN & HAYDEN MANGO SALSA

by Chef Paul Lamparelli

Serves 2 to 4

LAVENDER PEPPER-SPICED SHRIMP:

1 DOZEN	SHRIMP, WASHED, PEELED AND DE-VEINED

Season with Lavender Pepper Seasoning, Lavender Gourmet Seasoning, smoked paprika (or regular), cayenne pepper and salt, to taste. Sauté in olive oil.

GRILLED CORN & HAYDEN MANGO SALSA:

3 EARS	FRESH SWEET CORN
2 TBSP.	VEGETABLE OIL
	SALT AND PEPPER, TO TASTE
½	SWEET RED PEPPER, FINELY MINCED
½	RED ONION, FINELY MINCED
1	LARGE HAYDEN MANGO, PEELED AND FINELY DICED
3-5	MINT LEAVES, CHOPPED
2 TSP.	LAVENDER HONEY
1 TSP.	LAVENDER VINEGAR
1	ORANGE, JUICED

Rub corn with oil, and season with salt and pepper. Grill corn on barbecue (medium heat) until cooked and some brown and black spots have developed. Let corn cool and cut corn from cob into a salsa bowl. Add red pepper, red onion, mango and mint. In a separate bowl, whisk together honey, vinegar and orange juice. Mix with salsa ingredients and spoon over shrimp.

ENTRÉES

Lavender Crème Brûlée

By Chef Paul Lamparelli

Serves 6 to 8

4 c.	HEAVY CREAM
1 Tbsp.	CULINARY LAVENDER
8	EGG YOLKS
¾ c.	SUGAR, DIVIDED

Preheat oven to 300°F. Butter 6-oz. custard cups and set them into a shallow oven-proof roasting or baking pan. (If using a metal pan, cover the bottom of the pan with a layer of newspaper to ensure an even temperature on the bottom.)

In a large, heavy saucepan over medium heat, add cream and Culinary Lavender; heat just to a simmer. Remove from heat and allow lavender flowers to infuse with the cream for 5 minutes. Strain cream mixture through a fine-mesh strainer to remove lavender flowers.

In a large bowl, whisk together the egg yolks and ½ c. sugar until light and creamy. Slowly add the strained cream to the egg mixture, blend well. Divide custard mixture among the custard cups.

In a teapot or 1 quart liquid measuring cup, bring water for the water bath to a light simmer; carefully pour hot water into the baking pan to come half-way up the sides of the custard cups. NOTE: The most common mistake people make in baking custard is not putting enough water in the hot-water bath. The water should come up to the level of the custard inside the cups. You must protect your custard from the oven heat.

Bake 60 minutes, or until the custard is set around the edges but still loose in the center. The cooking time will depend largely on the size of the custard cups you are using, but begin checking after 30 minutes and check back regularly. When the center of the custard is just set, it will jiggle a little when shaken; that's when you can remove it from the oven.

Remove from oven and leave in the water bath until cooled. Remove cups from water bath and refrigerate at least 2 hours or up to 2 days.

When ready to serve, sprinkle approximately 2 tsp. of remaining sugar over each crème brûlée. Caramelize the top with a small, hand-held torch. Hold the torch 4 to 5 inches from the sugar, maintaining a slow and even motion. Stop torching just before the desired degree of doneness is reached, as the sugar will continue to cook for a few seconds after torching. If you don't have a torch, place crème brûlée 6 inches below the broiler for 4 to 6 minutes or until sugar bubbles and turns golden brown. Refrigerate crème brûlée at least 10 minutes before serving.

Pound Cake with Blueberries & Lavender Syrup

Serves 6 to 8

Pound Cake:

2 C.	ALL-PURPOSE FLOUR
½ TSP.	BAKING POWDER
¼ TSP.	SALT
2 STICKS	UNSALTED BUTTER, SOFTENED
1 ½ C.	SUGAR
3	LARGE EGGS, AT ROOM TEMPERATURE FOR 30 MINUTES
1 TSP.	FRESH LEMON ZEST, FINELY GRATED
1 TSP.	VANILLA
½ C.	WHOLE MILK, AT ROOM TEMPERATURE

Special equipment: 9" x 5" x 3" metal loaf pan

Put the oven rack in middle position and preheat oven to 350°F. Generously butter and flour 9" x 5" x 3" metal loaf pan, knocking out excess flour.

Whisk together flour, baking powder and salt. In a separate large bowl, beat together butter and sugar with an electric mixer at medium-high speed until light and fluffy (about 3 minutes in a stand mixer or 5 minutes with a hand-held mixer). Add eggs one at a time, beating well after each addition, then beat in zest and vanilla. Reduce speed to low and add flour mixture and milk alternately in batches, beginning and ending with flour and mixing until just incorporated. Spoon batter into loaf pan and bake until golden. It's done when a wooden pick or skewer inserted in center comes out with crumbs adhering (approximately 1 hour). Let the cake cool in the pan on a rack for 30 minutes, then invert onto rack and cool completely.

(Continued on page 94)

DESSERTS

(Continued from page 92)

LAVENDER SYRUP:

¾ C.	WATER
½ C.	SUGAR
4 TSP.	CULINARY LAVENDER (OR 2 TBSP. FRESH EDIBLE LAVENDER FLOWERS)
2 TSP.	FRESH LEMON JUICE
1 PINT	BLUEBERRIES

Bring water and sugar to a boil in a small saucepan, stirring until sugar is dissolved. Remove from heat and stir in lavender, then steep 30 minutes for Culinary Lavender or 40 minutes for fresh flowers. Pour syrup through a fine-mesh sieve into a bowl, discarding lavender. Stir in lemon juice and blueberries. Spoon berries and syrup over slices of cake just before serving.

Baker's notes:
Cake can be made 1 day ahead and cooled completely, then wrapped tightly in plastic wrap or kept in an airtight container at room temperature. Lavender syrup (without berries) can be made 2 hours ahead and kept covered at room temperature. Add berries just before serving.

Zesty Lavender Shortbread Wedges

Serves 8 to 10

½ C.	BUTTER AT ROOM TEMPERATURE
⅛ C.	SUGAR
⅛ C.	POWDERED SUGAR
1 TSP.	GRATED LEMON PEEL
1 TBSP.	LEMON JUICE
1 C.	ALL-PURPOSE FLOUR
½ TBSP.	CORNSTARCH
½ TSP.	CULINARY LAVENDER, GROUND (USE COFFEE GRINDER TO GRIND LAVENDER BUDS)
2 TBSP.	LAVENDER SUGAR (OPTIONAL)

Blend butter and sugars until creamy. Add remaining ingredients and mix until combined into a smooth dough. Press dough into two 8-inch pie dishes. Press tines of a fork around edges to make a ridge pattern. Pierce dough with fork in parallel lines about 1 inch apart. Bake until firm to touch and slightly browned, about 25 to 30 minutes. Sprinkle Lavender Sugar on dough while it's still hot (optional). Cut each round while still warm. Cool completely before serving.

DESSERTS

Lavender in Your Life

"THE GARDEN IS THE POOR MAN'S APOTHECARY."
GERMAN PROVERB

avender's uses are so diverse and plentiful that the herb is practically the star of some aromatherapy books. And many of the uses directed toward health maintenance and healing have been the subjects of serious scientific research that shows these are not just old wives' tales.

Research has found that lavender's calming qualities match some commonly prescribed sleeping medications. Lavender slows activity in the nervous system, while promoting relaxation and improving sleep quality. Studies suggest that a lavender pillow or a massage with lavender essential oil may reduce anxiety and lift the mood. In Germany, lavender flowers have been approved as a tea for insomnia, restlessness and nervous stomach irritations. Studies have even found it helpful with postoperative pain. Human clinical studies have reported that lavender essential oil may be beneficial in a variety of conditions, including insomnia, anxiety, stress, and as an antibacterial and antiviral agent. Lavender oil is also used together with other forms of integrative medicine, such as massage, acupuncture and chiropractic manipulation.

Lavender is a key ingredient for many who practice aromatherapy, the healing use of essential oils extracted from certain species of plants. Of some 300 essential oils used by aromatherapy practitioners today, lavender oil is said to be one of about 10 that would provide an average household with most of its needs. It is one of several known as "adaptogens," essential oils that help the body achieve a state of balance. A gentle sniff or two will help when you are too wired to relax, while a stronger concentration of scent will be stimulating.

Lavender can be used to treat headaches, as a healing bath for circulatory disorders, or in massage for sore joints. Lavender oil is good for treating burns, wounds, eczema, acne and other skin ailments, such as fungal infections like candidiasis.

In this chapter you will find some specific ways to use lavender for your health. These are tried-and-true simple remedies, but remember, these recommendations require the use of common sense. Lavender and other herbs clearly have some powerful properties; otherwise, why would we bother to use them? Therefore, it is important to exercise caution, especially with internal use. While there are no known scientific reports of interactions between lavender and conventional medications, its relaxing properties could potentially enhance the effects of central nervous system depressants such as pain and anti-anxiety medications. Too much of a good thing can be bad, so talk to your doctor before using lavender if you are taking prescription medications. The information presented here is not meant to take the place of diagnosis and treatment by qualified medical practitioner. See your doctor if your ailment is acute or persistent.

The healing benefits of lavender range from the soothing fragrance of the fresh herb to lavender-filled sleeping masks.

Some people are actually allergic to lavender. They can get nausea, headaches or chills from inhalation or skin absorption. Although some suggest that pregnant women use lavender to treat flatulence and indigestion, and to prevent stretch marks, some medical experts say pregnant and breast-feeding women should avoid using lavender; it is said to be a uterine stimulant. Some experts say lavender products should not be given to children internally; others say even colicky babies can

safely be given a very weak infusion to calm irritability. Again, if you want to use lavender in these cases, consult your physician.

Like other essential oils, lavender is quickly and effectively absorbed into the skin. Though it is one of the few essential oils which may be used "neat," or undiluted, on the skin, try a tiny drop to be sure the oil is not an irritant. Lavender essential oil should be used sparingly and will be easier to spread if you mix with a base oil, such as almond, olive or corn oil. Always avoid the eyes and mucous membranes.

With these caveats in mind, lavender has a long history of beneficial use. How much you incorporate it into your life depends on how much you love it and on how much time and energy you want to spend. Lavender use can be as simple as buying a lotion for after the bath or a sweet-scented bag of dried flowers to tuck under your pillow on restless nights. A small bottle of essential oil is like a first-aid kit in itself, useful for dabbing "neat" on burns, scrapes or insect bites.

Or, if you fall in love with lavender—it inspires your imagination, and just being around it makes you feel good— you can go deep into aromatherapy, mixing lavender with other essential oils to custom-make remedies for everything from aching joints to acne to your dog's flea problems. Often, aromatherapists add other essential oils to create a synergistic mixture in which the different oils combine into a powerful compound that is different from its component parts. You'll need to study aromatherapy texts to learn the proper proportions for these mixtures. Check your local library or bookstore for books on herbs and aromatherapy to learn about these more intensive uses of lavender. Because of the power of herbs, it is particularly important to consult expert sources before using lavender or any other herb internally.

"I work in a medical office at a Harvard teaching hospital in Cambridge, Massachusetts. I order lavender oil and sachets to have on hand for my patients. I find when I take their blood pressure and find it high, I just dab a bit of oil under their noses, and it can lower their blood pressure. I also give the purple boxes to my patients who may be feeling a bit blue."

Once you're ready, you can grow your own plants and even learn to distill your own essential oil. Or just use the flowers, stems and leaves in a variety of charming craft projects. All the parts of this plant are useful!

For most folks, the simple ideas described below will be enough to provide many of the benefits of this marvelous plant. But first, some definitions and instructions for common ways of preparing herbs for use:

Decoction An extract produced by boiling roots, barks and twigs. Heat the herb in water and simmer for up to an hour, until the volume has been reduced by one third. Strain and store in a cool place. Decoctions should be made fresh each day.

Infusion Leaves and flowers steeped in hot water, as in making tea. Bring water almost to the boiling point and pour over the herbs in a pot with a close-fitting lid. Let the mixture infuse for 10 minutes. Strain and store in a cool place. Make a fresh infusion each day.

Syrup A decoction or infusion made with sugar or honey. Heat the infusion or decoction in a sauce pan, add honey or unrefined sugar and stir until dissolved. When the mixture is cool, pour it into a dark glass bottle and seal with a cork stopper.

Tincture An alcohol or water-alcohol solution of a medicinal substance. Making a tincture is a complicated procedure, one most folks don't attempt. You can buy tinctures at your local health food store or pharmacy. If you want to try it yourself: Steep the fresh or dried herb in a 25-percent mixture of alcohol and water. Do not use industrial alcohol, methyl alcohol or rubbing alcohol (isopropyl alcohol) in tincture making—they are all extremely toxic. Ethyl alcohol is used for commercial tinctures, but diluted spirits such as vodka are suitable for home use. The herb and vodka/water mixture is sealed in a jar and stored in a cool place for two weeks, then pushed through a wine press.

Distillation On a commercial level, there are two main methods used to derive essential oils from plants—hydro- and steam distillation. In hydro-distillation, water and plant material are boiled together, producing a "hydrosol," rather than a pure essential oil. In steam distillation, dry steam vaporizes and extracts the oil. As the steam passes up through the plant materials, it carries the oil and other plant essences into a receiving container. This distillate cools, and essential oils float to the top and are siphoned away, leaving behind a hydrosol. You can do this with a pressure cooker on top of the kitchen stove, but only a few drops of oil will be produced, so unless you're curious and want to experiment, you're probably better off just buying commercially produced oil.

Healing Your Body

Lavender is antibiotic, antispasmodic, analgesic, antiseptic, antiviral and antifungal, which means that there are many ways it can be used to protect and promote health. The oil, an essential for home first-aid kits, maintains its therapeutic powers for about two years. After that, use it for its fragrance, perhaps as part of your housecleaning routine. Here are a few healing ways to use lavender, its essential oil and related products.

> *"... especially good use for all the griefes and paines of the head and brain."*
>
> JOHN PARKINSON

Aches and pains A massage can relax muscles and promote circulation, and a lavender-scented massage lotion will make the experience even more relaxing.

Acne-prone skin Soak a cotton ball with witch hazel, add a drop of lavender oil and rub over the troubled area.

Blisters A drop of essential oil on an open blister will prevent infection. Be prepared: it will sting!

Burns and scalds For minor burns only; seek medical aid for more serious injuries or any electrical burn. If the burn is minor, immediately run cool (*not ice cold*) water over the burn for several minutes. Then put two drops of lavender oil directly onto the burn. You may also put a few drops on a piece of sterile cloth or gauze and cover the burn.

Cold sores Dab with a mix of 10 drops of lavender oil and a tablespoon of a carrier oil, such as almond, olive or canola.

Ear infections Persistent earaches that don't respond to antibiotic treatment sometimes can be helped by the old-fashioned remedy of a piece of cotton wool soaked in a teaspoon of pure virgin olive oil, mixed with one drop of lavender essential oil. Be sure to squeeze out the excess oil before putting the cotton wool into the ear.

Gum disease Rinse the mouth once daily with warm water containing a drop of lavender essential oil. *Do not swallow.*

Headaches and migraines Add two or three drops of lavender oil to a carrier oil and massage into the temples and nape of the neck. For migraines, follow up with an infusion made from the flowers. *Important: See a physician for a sudden, persistent headache.*

Headache, depression or insomnia for adults or children Use two to four drops of oil in two to three cups of boiling water; inhale the vapors.

Scrapes and cuts Aromatherapists say lavender causes such quick healing that you should not use the essential oil on open wounds that may still have dirt or other infectious material in them. You may wash a scrape with a solution of five to 10 drops of lavender oil to a pint of warm water. Repeat a few hours later. If you use a bandage, a drop of neat lavender oil on the bandage will help the wound heal quickly and without a scar.

Stings Whether it's an insect, a plant or a jellyfish sting, apply drops of neat lavender oil one at a time every five minutes, up to a total of 10 drops.

Stressed out? Relax with a cup of lavender tea One to two teaspoons of whole herb per cup of hot water. Steep for 10 to 15 minutes.

In Your Home

Lavender's scent—sweet yet earthy and fresh—can make a home feel warm, welcoming and well cared for. Homemakers through the ages have used lavender to freshen the air, disinfect surfaces and repel insects. A bonus: lavender's anti-anxiety properties will lend an air of relaxation as well. Try a few of these simple methods in your own home.

Freshen the air
- Fill a spray bottle with warm water and a few drops of lavender essential oil, shake well and use it as you would any room freshener. (Be sure not to spray it on wood.) Lightly mist your bedclothes for a soothing scent at bedtime.
- Put a drop of essential oil on a cold light bulb, where it will radiate fragrance as the bulb heats up. The oil is flammable, so don't drop it onto a hot bulb.
- Make your own defuser: Buy wooden shish kabob sticks and cut them in half. Put lavender oil into a pretty little bottle and stand the sticks in the oil for a long-lasting scent.
- A fresh bouquet of lavender blossoms is beautiful and fragrant. Or fill a bowl with lavender buds and set it close to

your favorite chair, where you can easily reach over to stir and squeeze the buds to release their scent.

Cleaning and disinfecting Add a few drops of oil to the final rinse water when you clean kitchen counters or floors. Add a few drops to a bottle of dish-washing liquid. Soak dishtowels or sponges in boiling water to which you have added a drop of lavender oil, then wash in the machine.

Sweeten your clothes Put a few drops of oil on a small square of cloth and toss it into the dryer. Put a few drops onto small cotton wool balls and tuck them into drawers. Your clothes will be fragrant, and the lavender will discourage moths. Put one drop of essential oil into the spray bottle you use when ironing.

A fragrant bathroom Use your lavender spray bottle for the final rinse after cleaning, or put a couple of drops on a cloth to wipe surfaces. Try a drop of oil on the cardboard of the toilet paper roll.

Growing your own? Make a sleep pillow by stitching a small piece of material on three sides and stuff with fresh, dried lavender flowers, then hand stitch the fourth side, or tie it with a ribbon. Make a sachet by filling a pretty handkerchief with flowers, folding envelope style and tying with a ribbon. No place to grow your own lavender? Stuff a sleep pillow with any kind of crushed, dried leaf and scent it with essential oil. Or tuck these pillows into a pair of shoes, or hang from a ribbon in your closet.

Scented air If you are a candlemaker, simply add a few drops of essential oil to the wax. Or buy unscented candles, light the candle, and when the wax begins to melt add oil to the wax. Be careful! The oil is flammable, so do not put it directly onto the wick.

Scented stationery Cut up a paper tissue or a piece of cotton cloth and put a drop of oil on each piece. Scatter the pieces among the stationery and envelopes you want to scent, and seal it all in a plastic bag for at least 24 hours. Good to use for love letters and other happy messages!

Barbecue flavors Soak a few lavender stems in water, then lay them atop the coals to add a special flavor to your meat.

Fragrant fireplace Toss a few dried stems into your fireplace; there's nothing on this plant that can't be used to contribute a sweet scent!

Pet care A few drops of lavender oil brushed into your pet's coat helps get rid of fleas, and lavender water is good for cleaning out wounds on dogs or cats.

Doll Up or Relax

Want to bathe like the ancient Greeks and Romans? For a stimulating lavender bath, make a sachet by filling a square or circle of cheesecloth or muslin with lavender flowers and tying it securely. Hang the bag under the running hot water as you fill the tub, squeezing occasionally to release the oils. Allow it to steep in the bathwater.

If you prefer a shower, wash as usual, then add a few drops of essential oil to your washcloth and rub yourself all over while standing under the shower, breathing deeply to take advantage of the aromatic steam.

Help skin cells regenerate by either of the bathing methods above, or by using lavender products as face and body moisturizers.

Put two drops of lavender oil into a bowl of steaming water,

Whether it's a homemade soap bar or store-bought bath bomb, lavender's calming scent and natural cleaning and healing agents are pluses in any bathroom.

cover your head with a towel, and spend a few minutes leaning over the steaming bowl. Finish by splashing with cold water. This is best for normal skin and shouldn't be done if you have sunburn or other inflammation, broken veins or sensitive skin.

Make an old-fashioned perfumed soap ball by grating one large bar of simple, unscented soap or Castile soap. Add a quarter cup of rosewater and let it soak for 15 minutes. Combine the mixture in an electric blender, or use a mortar and pestle, and add three drops of lavender oil, one drop at a time.

Make your own bath salts with washing soda crystals, plus a few drops each of food coloring and lavender oil.

Make a hair rinse with two drops of oil per tablespoon of natural cider vinegar and add to the final rinse after you wash your hair.

Crafts and Things

Perhaps those London ladies (left) were buying lavender sprigs for one of the traditional crafts described below, still a pleasant way to spend relaxing time while making something to beautify your home. Lavender offers a double reward to those who use it in crafts projects: lovely fragrance and soothing, subtle colors. It is a favorite component of these crafts—wand, tussie-mussie, potpourri and wreath—but you can also simply tie a little bouquet of lavender to a basket or gift to add a special touch.

Lavender Wands

Lavender wands can be used to scent linen and to decorate packages, or can be given as gifts. They are not as tricky to put together as they look and can even be made by children.

You will need

- Freshly gathered lavender stems, at least a foot long, with top blossoms that are just beginning to open. Each wand uses an uneven number of stems—13, 15 or 17 are good numbers.
- A yard or more of narrow ribbon

Directions

- Strip off the leaves and the lowest flowers on each stem so that you have four to five inches of blossoms on the stem.
- Tie the stems tightly together just below the flower heads with one end of the ribbon.
- Turn the bunch upside down and carefully bend the stems down over the flowers, one at a time. Starting at that bend, weave the ribbon over and under the stems to create a

basket effect. The first couple of ribbon rows will be the hardest; it's easier once you get the stems under control.

- Work your way down until the entire length of blossoms is enclosed in this stem-and-ribbon basket.
- Wind the ribbon around the remaining stems a few times and tie a slip-knot and bow.
- Trim the ends of the stems. You may also continue the ribbon down farther, binding the stems, and make a loop to hang up the wand.

Tussie-Mussies

Lavender flowers and leaves are a fragrant and traditional addition to a tussie-mussie, the little bouquet that was popular during Victorian times, yet still so charming to make, or receive, anytime.

Flowers have been worn as decoration for centuries, beginning with the garlands and wreaths of ancient Greece and Rome, and, of course, Hawai'i has a long tradition of lei making with a variety of plant materials. Small bouquets have been a part of many cultures. Aztec nobles carried them. Medieval city dwellers kept them close at hand to ward off the stench of cities, where bathing was infrequent, animals were everywhere and clothing was seldom washed. Elegant Europeans of the 1600s, male and female, wore boutonnières or tucked nosegays into tight bodices. Small bouquets pinned to the bosom, suspended on a chain or decorating a towering powdered wig provided a fresh and fragrant accent to the elaborate clothing of the upper classes. And even the poorest could bind together artful bunches of wildflowers and sprigs of garden herbs to carry to church, present to a sweetheart or give to a neighbor on May Day.

> *"Odors have an altogether peculiar force, in affecting us through association; a force differing essentially from that of objects addressing the touch, the taste, the sight or the hearing."*
>
> EDGAR ALLAN POE

Somewhere along the line, these small, compact bouquets with bound stems came to be called tussie-mussies. No one seems to know the origin of the word, which has gone through lots of different variations. It was first recorded in about 1440, when it was written as tusmose. In later centuries, the spelling became tuzzy-muzzy, and now is usually tussie-mussie.

Perhaps no other culture has displayed such fascination with the tussie-mussie as that of the Victorians. By the time of the ascension of the young Queen Victoria to the British throne in 1837, the tussie-mussie had grown beyond its original medical/preventive use of warding off the smells and plagues of city life to become a fashion accessory and a carrier of romantic messages, usually wrapped in a lace doily and tied with a ribbon.

Tussie-mussies can be made with almost any plant material. Look for foliage with a variety of texture and color.

In the days of Victoria, flowers were all the rage. Girls judged too young for jewels wore fresh flowers to parties. Men put flowers in their buttonholes, and women tied tussie-mussies to their wrists, attached them to hair or bonnet, or carried them as nosegays. Posy holders or "bosom bottles" pinned to the bodice provided a convenient container where stems could be kept wet to preserve the flowers' freshness. Ladies took up botanical drawing and studied botany, a craze which allowed them to exercise their brains by learning plants' relationships and their Latin names at a time when women's intellectual lives often were limited by cultural expectations.

In this world, the "language of flowers" flourished. No blossom, leaf or herb was without meaning. Tussie-mussies were used to send discrete messages to be decoded by the gift's recipient. This language, which came to full flowering in the 19th century, drew on many sources. Some plants and flowers had acquired symbolism over centuries of use in the West, from mythology, religion and medicine. Poets drew on these well-known symbols to add layers of meaning to their work. For example, Shakespeare used floral symbolism often; perhaps the best-known example is Ophelia's speech in *Hamlet*: "There's rosemary, that's for remembrance; pray you, love, remember."

In the early 1800s, books describing this language began to circulate, becoming so popular that it is said 57 writers produced 98 books on the language of flowers between 1800 and 1937. These books, with long lists of flower names paired with their symbolic meanings, often were beautifully illustrated. When combined with the Victorian fondness for giving and carrying tussie-mussies, this language provided a socially acceptable way for lovers to pursue their courtship in these prim times. The gift of a tussie-mussie would send the recipient straight to her book of flower vocabulary to decipher the romantic meaning of the bouquet.

Had a suitor sent a tussie-mussie with a red rose surrounded by sprigs of lavender and ivy? His swooning sweetheart could translate this as, "I love you, devotion, wedded love."

On the other hand, one who wished to send a message could look at another list in which sentiments were arranged alphabetically. To express the pain of a broken heart, a rejected swain might choose a yellow lily (falsehood) along with willow (forsaken) and once again lavender, in this case symbolizing distrust!

Lavender, in its symbolism as well as its uses, is a versatile plant. One author's list of the meanings for lavender includes devotion, luck, success, happiness, distrust, ardent attachment and soothes the tremblings and passions of the heart.

Whatever its intended meaning in a particular tussie-mussie, lavender's flowers or silvery leaves certainly added a pleasant fragrance to the bouquet. And its ability to lift spirits and calm the nerves made it a helpful attribute in a bouquet prepared, or received, by a young lover caught in the throes of passionate attraction.

Though tussie-mussies are famous for their romantic symbolism, they are also welcome and appropriate gifts at any time—to console a sick friend, to thank a hostess, or to congratulate a new mother, for example.

For special occasions, such as Mother's Day, tussie-mussies can be made with herbs such as rosemary, lavender and camellias. Like lavender, rosemary and camellias have several meanings. Rosemary can mean fidelity, devotion, wisdom, and, of course, remembrance. Camellias stand for excellence, beauty, and contentment. What a lovely message to give your mother on her special day—or to any loved one on any day, for that matter! For an extra personal touch, add a little scroll to the Mother's Day bouquet to explain the significance of the flowers, making the sentimental gesture especially touching for both maker and recipient. Scrolls or cards with the symbolism of the bouquet's flowers and herbs are especially important in these days when few understand the hidden connotations. And since so many tussie-mussie ingredients, like lavender, roses and camellias, have multiple connotations, a written explanation could save misinterpretation if the recipient tries to look them up.

> *"As rosemary is to the spirit, so lavender is to the soul."*
>
> ANONYMOUS

Making Your Own Tussie-Mussie

Making a tussie-mussie always starts with one special central blossom or a bunch of blossoms—perhaps a single rose or a tight bunch of lavender flowers—that is then surrounded by fresh herbs, flowers and greenery. A tussie-mussie generally uses more greenery and herbs than a regular bouquet, which may include only flowers.

You will need
- Various flowers, leaves and herbs. Don't forget the lavender!
- Scissors and hand pruners
- Yarn, florist's wire or tape or pipe cleaners

- Paper doilies
- Plastic wrap or aluminum foil
- Cotton balls or sphagnum moss
- A glass of water to hold flowers
- Narrow ribbon

Directions

- Place the plant materials in the glass of water. Remove them one at a time to strip remaining leaves from the stems, and clip the stems to about four or five inches.
- Choose the most important flower to be placed in the center of the tussie-mussie. Hold it in your left hand.
- Surround the central flower with several sprigs of another flower or herb, preferably small pieces in a color that contrasts with your central flower.

- Continue to add concentric rings of herbs and small flowers. Use the yarn or other binding material to hold the stems together as you go.
- When you have a pleasantly full but compact little bouquet, surround it with a circle of foliage such as geranium or ivy leaves. Finish binding the stems down to the bottom.
- To keep the tussie-mussie fresh, place the stem bottoms into cotton balls or sphagnum moss soaked in water, and wrap the end of the bouquet in plastic wrap or aluminum foil.
- Cut a hole in the middle of the doily, either by folding it several times and cutting off a tiny bit of the point which is formed or by cutting an X in the middle of the doily.
- Insert the bound stems into the hole and push the doily up so that it cups the foliage. Be sure to keep the doily dry.
- Wrap the stems with florist's tape, catching the paper doily and covering the plastic wrap or aluminum foil completely to make a little handle. Use the ribbon to tie a bow on the handle.

Write a sweet note explaining the significance of the flowers and herbs you've chosen, and present it with love to the lucky recipient!

Potpourri

Lavender is a treasured ingredient in potpourri, a long-lasting mix of dried herbs and other materials that has been used for centuries to scent the home. Such delicacies are perhaps less needed today than they were long ago, when plumbing was primitive, animals shared the house, and people went for months without a bath, often wearing the same clothes through the winter. But the fragrance of potpourri is still a pleasure.

"Everybody needs beauty as well as bread, places to play in and pray in, where nature may heal and give strength to body and soul."

JOHN MUIR

The old way to make potpourri is the moist method, a very strong-smelling and long-lasting potpourri, but not a pretty one. This kind of mixture is the origin of the name potpourri, which means "rotten pot." These potpourris are usually put into covered containers that have a few holes in the top to allow the scent to escape, or a lid that is removed from time to time. Moist potpourri are made by mixing dried flowers (such as rose petals, geranium leaves and lavender flowers), and then layering these with a mixture of salt and spices, which then may be moistened with brandy or lemon juice. These and other types of potpourri also need a fixative, usually cut or powdered orris root or calamus root, which may be purchased from potpourri suppliers. The fixative absorbs the essential oils and perfumes of the recipe.

Though moist potpourri is still a great way to create a scent, most people are probably more familiar with the dried version. Again, the main ingredients are scented flower petals, leaves and other botanical material, but these are chosen in part for their beauty and color, because unlike a moist potpourri, the dried potpourri is usually visible in an open bowl or basket. Dried potpourri, like the moist, can also contain other ingredients like woods, roots and barks, spices, seeds and citrus peel. Dried flowers and leaves are not intense enough to perfume a room for long, so essential oils are often added for a stronger scent. Because the potpourri will be on view, you might want to press a few flowers to scatter around the top, or use silica gel crystals or glycerin to preserve whole flowers with their color and shape intact.

Dried potpourri may also be used to make sachets or cushions, and in this case, it doesn't really matter how they look—the fragrance is what you're after. You'll want to crush the materials so that they are powdery before you stuff the fabric, adding some extra powdered orris root scented with lavender oil.

And of course, a few drops of oil will revive a tired sachet.

Some people like to make simmering or stove-top potpourri. Steamers are available especially for this purpose, or you can just use an old saucepan (dedicated to potpourri use), especially if you have a wood stove burning. Use a mixture that is heavy on seeds and leaves, boosted with essential oil and orris root fixative. Prepare the mixture a couple of days before you plan to use it, and if you want to reuse the mixture, strain it and let it dry thoroughly between uses. You may put the potpourri mixture into little fabric bundles to make it easy to fish them out, and these bundles, suitably wrapped in pretty material and tied with a ribbon, also make a nice gift.

Potpourri is a good gift in any case, whether you put it in a pretty container or a lace or fabric sachet. To make it a truly long-lasting gift, include a little bottle of lavender essential oil so the recipient can liven up the potpourri as the scent fades.

Making Your Own Potpourri

Like cooking, potpourri-making offers a seemingly endless variety of possibilities. The choice of flowers and other ingredients will depend on your own taste and on what you can find in your garden or your neighborhood; lavender flowers and essential oil are among the most common ingredients. Check your local library or bookstore for books filled with recipes, crafts ideas and lovely photographs of potpourri mixtures to inspire you. Or simply experiment with the ingredients you have on hand, following the general directions that follow for a dry potpourri that can be displayed in a bowl or basket or crushed for use in sachets or other craft projects.

Potpourri sachets can freshen the air anywhere—lingerie drawer, bathroom, luggage or even the car.

You will need

- Two glass or ceramic mixing bowls—one small, one large; plastic or wood will retain scents and should be avoided.
- An airtight container for storage
- Glass or metal measuring cups and spoons
- Metal spoons for mixing
- A variety of dried scented and decorative plant materials. These could be flowers, bark, seeds, aromatic garden foliage, citrus peel, spices or herbs.
- A fixative, such as cut orris root
- One or more essential oils

Directions

- Collect your ingredients, perhaps drying them as they become available and storing them in a warm, dry place until you are ready to prepare your potpourri. How you dry each ingredient will depend on its individual qualities. Herbs like lavender and many flowers may be tied together with an elastic band and hung in a dry, airy place. Fragile flowers or those that you would like to preserve for decoration, along with fruits, berries and citrus peels, should be dried flat on sheets of paper or muslin or on a screen-covered frame.
- Begin your mixture by placing fixative and essential oil into the small bowl. Mix well. A good proportion is about one teaspoon of essential oil and one tablespoon of cut orris root for every cup of botanical material.
- Place the bulk dry ingredients—flowers, herbs, spices—in the large mixing bowl. (Save special decorative flowers in a dry place.)
- Pour the ingredients of the small bowl into the dry ingredients and mix thoroughly with a spoon.
- Store the mixture in the airtight container in a dark, dry place for several weeks, shaking or stirring daily for the first week and about twice a week thereafter.
- Transfer the "mature" potpourri to an attractive container and top it off

with the decorative dried flowers. Save any leftover potpourri mix in the sealed container.

A word of caution: Remember to keep essential oils out of the hands of children and to avoid skin contact with the oils yourself (though lavender oil is safe, most essential oils should not be used on the skin undiluted). If you tend to have allergies, work where there is good ventilation and consider wearing a mask when handling botanical materials.

A Simple Wreath

Wreath making can be as fancy as you want it to be, and can be made with a variety of garden plants and flowers. But of course, lavender is the base for everything, and you can make a lovely pure lavender wreath fairly simply.

You will need

- Flowering lavender. This wreath requires a lot of stems, so you'll probably want to do it when your own plants bloom or after buying bunches on a trip to a lavender farm.
- A circular base for the wreath, perhaps the willow or grapevine versions you can find in any craft store.
- Moss, if you want to plump up the wreath.
- Elastic bands and a ball of twine or raffia.

Directions

- Grasp your lavender by the handful and arrange the stems so that all the flowers are bunched closely together.
- Cut the stems a few inches below the blossoms and secure them with an elastic band.
- Lay the bunch along the wreath base and wrap the twine or raffia around the base and a lavender bunch, pulling it snug.
- Lay the next bunch overlapping the stems of the first, and tightly wrap the twine around to bind it to the base.
- Continue layering bunches all the way around, with the flowers pointing all in the same direction.
- Tuck in the end of the twine or raffia beneath the first bundle.
- Make a loop for hanging and attach it to the base.
- Let the wreath lay flat as it dries, so that the flower bunches don't droop or sag.

Making wreaths can be an enjoyable group activity, during the holidays or any time of the year.

You can tie a pretty bow to your wreath, or tuck in other dried flowers or some baby's breath. It will last for several years; add a few drops of essential oil to the back of the wreath if the scent begins to fade. ⟨∭⟩

CHAPTER FIVE

The Lessons of Lavender

"I GO TO NATURE TO BE SOOTHED AND HEALED,
AND TO HAVE MY SENSES PUT IN ORDER."
JOHN BURROUGHS

In its fantastic location, with its thriving plants and welcoming hosts, Ali'i Kula Lavender celebrates life and living things, beauty and sweetness, healing and growth. "Stop and smell the lavender," says one of the signs tucked in amid the flowers. And another, a Chinese proverb carved on a plaque at the feet of a bronze Chinese water carrier, sums up the spirit of this place: "He who plants a garden plants happiness."

One of Ali'i Kula Lavender's hosts is **Lani Medina Weigert**. Here is her story: Similar to Alii's childhood, Lani grew up gardening with her grandmother on the windward coast of O'ahu. Her grandmother was Emily Kanamu Atkins Ka'ahanui.

Lani Medina Weigert: "To build a dream and fulfill a passion."

"There were many afternoons while I was growing up in Kailua, on the windward side of O'ahu, when I'd sit on the grass and watch my grandmother care for the plants in our yard," Lani remembers. "I could hear her murmuring under her breath, as if talking to the weeds and flowers … or maybe she was praying. Looking back, I see the roots of my own spiritual awakening taking hold in my grandmother's presence—all of it conveyed at a level deeper than language. Grandma Emily understood English but never spoke a word of it, and I understood everything she said to me without speaking any Hawaiian. Her love was conveyed through her eyes, her teachings passed on through her actions."

On one of their lazy afternoons together, when Lani was about 8 years old, she and Grandma and were relaxing on a *hāli'i* (mat) under a papaya tree looking up to a sunny, cloudless sky. Without any warning, Grandma stood up and told Lani in a rushed tone that they had to take down the clothes on clothesline right away. No sooner did they get all the clothes plucked from the line and into the house than the raindrops fell one by one like bullets onto the flat, tin roof.

Amazed, Lani looked at her grandmother, but Grandma said nothing. "In her silence I understood that I needed to listen more and talk less," she says. "As I got older, I too could smell the rain coming; I too began to feel the temperature shift and the wind telling me what was coming. And all because I had learned to listen, to sense, to be in tune with the world around me … the very same world that so many people don't truly see or hear or experience."

When Lani was a high school junior at Kamehameha Schools, she met a special young man named Noland. His enthusiasm for music was contagious, and he was to become a remarkable musician (now widely known as Brother Noland). "I am honored to have served as an inspiration for some of his compositions," Lani says. "My journey with Noland spanned over 11 years; we married and had a beautiful daughter, Pomaika'imahina. As in all special relationships, we both grew to become better versions of ourselves as a result of the bond. Lessons we knew became even clearer in the sharing of them. When the time came to go our separate ways to continue our mutual quests for higher learning, we were saddened, but accepted it as our spiritual destiny."

Early one morning in January 2002, Lani's girlfriend Mars (short for the French name, Marseu) picked her up to go to hula class and mentioned that they would be making a short side trip to

Kula to pick up a few lavender wreaths that she had ordered as gifts.

The two women worked together at a large tour company that encompassed operations on Maui, the Big Island of Hawaiʻi and Kauaʻi. Lani was in sales and marketing, and Mars Simpson handled operations. But their friendship extended far beyond work; they had been dear friends since 1986, and Mars had served as a catalyst in several of Lani's life changes. Mars is a native of Rotuma, a small Polynesian island located near the islands of Fiji in the South Pacific, where she was raised with cultural beliefs similar to those of Hawaiians. In addition to being close associates at work, the two women went on snorkel excursions, attended *lūʻau* together and swapped books on psychology, wellness and spirituality.

On the way up to pick up the lavender, the two friends drove up the slopes of Haleakalā until they reached a rusty old cattle guard, then up a narrow driveway to a charming country cottage, a stylish and rustic dwelling painted a light sage color with white French doors. The woman inside turned out to be an old friend of Mars'. She explained that the wreaths were not quite done yet, and she needed some time to put the finishing touches on them. Already, these handmade lavender wreaths were beautiful to look at, and they smelled wonderful.

Just then, the friendly face of a tanned, local man with a tattered, well-worn cap emerged from the door. He had eyes that sparkled and a smile as warm as a hug. "Aloha, my name is Alii, and I'm the caretaker," he said. Seeing that their wreaths were not ready, he quickly offered to show the women around his farm.

"I could tell he was a spirited Hawaiian soul who exuded pure aloha," Lani says. Feeling an immediate kinship with this friendly man, they obediently followed as he called, "Baby" (pronounced *BeBe*), "We going this way."

"What we saw next was the closest thing to heavenly beauty you could get and still be on Earth," Lani remembers. "At 4,000 feet elevation, we were treated to an expansive view of south and central Maui that stretched straight out over the ocean to the horizon. You could see forever. Majestic Haleakalā rose to greet the clouds, with rolling hills in every hue of green. Cool breezes danced through the many varieties of proteas, hydrangea, geraniums, impatiens, lilies, bromeliads and roses. This was a full buffet of colors and textures that heightened all my senses.

From 4,000 feet, visitors to the lavender farm enjoy expansive views of south and central Maui.

Sun-kissed, blue-gray lavender, in neat patches around the farm, offered up a heady fragrance that floated through the air. The gentle breezes, the beautiful vistas, the peaceful quiet, gave us the unforgettable gift of seeing the world we knew in a completely different way. The beauty was stunning, and the feeling was euphoric. The sense of place was undeniably spiritual."

Alii exuded natural wisdom, displaying a deep reverence for life and a heartfelt appreciation for nature. As he talked, Lani felt a gentle stirring. "Oh my gosh, I think I'm supposed to be here," she thought.

She looked at Alii and spontaneously said, "Am I supposed to be here?"

He replied, without missing a beat, "Yes, bebe, I don't know what took you so long!"

Amazed by his response, she probed further. "Do you want me to bring people up here?"

"Yes," he said with a cheerful certainty.

"How many people?" she asked.

"Plennny," he answered.

And so a business was born.

"Call it destiny, call it coincidence; I truly believed that all the events in my life led me here," Lani says. "With this spirited farmer, I saw an opportunity to build a dream and to fulfill a passion."

Over several nights, Lani pondered over questions such as: *What would they do with the lavender? How could she get people to come to this blessed place? What was her higher vision for the lavender farm?*

"I didn't have many answers about making lavender a viable business," she says, "but two words kept coming to my mind—experience and land."

It wasn't the lavender that people would come for at first; it would be the *experience*. And the experience had to create a personal feeling of connection and pleasure—a feeling so uplifting that people would return again and again. Day after day, she sat quietly in the sun amid the sprawling lavender fields in Kula, listening, watching and waiting for inspiration from the land itself. She searched for a strategic vision in the whispered messages between the trees, the flowers, the wind and the soil.

Not surprisingly, purple is a predominant color at Aliʻi Kula Lavender, from employee apparel to garden features.

If someone other than Alii had been her new business partner, he might sooner have locked her up than to listen. But listening intently was the key, and Alii, the farmer, knew that better than anyone. "I had to let the land speak to me," Lani says. "The joy and inner peace I felt as I came to know this parcel of land was something I wanted to recreate for visitors."

She imagined an experience that was healing, rejuvenating and memorable beyond words. She imagined a place that would beckon people from all over the world with friendship, hospitality and fun. To accomplish so much on the spiritual level while succeeding as a business was an audacious vision. "Sometimes I wondered if Alii and I were dreaming too big, or trying to do too much. But the more I learned about the lavender plant itself, and how utterly versatile it is in its applications—as an antiseptic, analgesic, fungicide, fragrance and food— the more I saw that our multidimensional mission was a great match with our multidimensional product."

Lavender plants can't thrive unless the soil and atmospheric conditions are right. Neither can dreams. Lani knew that it was time to create a business model conducive to the farm's environment. "Successful independent farmers, like all successful and original people I know, seemed to have their heads in the clouds and their feet planted firmly on the ground," Lani says." It's a dichotomy that, to this day, fits who we are and what we do."

For Lani, the vision required a journey that ended with her own feet planted in the Kula soil. At first, she promoted the lavender farm while continuing her regular job.

"After 28 years, I was very much ingrained in the tour and travel business," she says. "But people slowly started to think of me in terms of lavender. Hotel managers requested lavender products for their amenity baskets. Rental car companies asked me if they could put the farm on their maps for customers."

Lani's part-time sales effort was so successful, it compelled her to make lavender her full-time gig. "It was a bit scary to go from a corporate salary to a little farm, where I was responsible of generating an income I could live on," Lani says. "But I also needed to get into the sailboat and sail out until I couldn't see the harbor!"

The voyage was successful. By spring of 2004, the pieces were in place for a new business with a unique business plan.

Lani's marketing skills helped her to promote Alii's agricultural and artistic talents. For the crafts sector of the business, Mars decided to join the company. With her interest in the product development and operations, Mars took over the day-to-day running of the business. "Mars likes it when things are operating efficiently," Lani says, with a grin. "That's what makes her passionate."

Alii continues to care for the plants and facilities, Lani brings in the visitors, and Mars makes sure everything functions as it should. "It's a good fit," Lani says, "We don't overlap in our areas. We come together to tell each other what we're doing, get all excited, and run out and go again!"

The three partners changed the company name from Nanea a'o Kula to Ali'i Kula Lavender, which refers both to the farm's founder and to the royal connections of this purple-flowered plant.

For Alii, growing lavender feels as if he is carrying on a tradition which,

although not native to Hawai'i, was beloved by Hawai'i's royalty. Great adapters of foreign customs, aristocrats who embraced the refined and regal court life of their European peers, the *ali'i* (Hawaiian royalty) who ruled Hawai'i during its brief monarchy surely grew and used this fragrant and versatile herb. Now Alii is its steward.

Yet with all his sense of tradition, Alii is a forward-thinking business man. "He thrives on change," Lani says. "To him, it means things are growing."

To this day, Alii gives Lani the freedom to grow the business. "There are no questions asked," she says. "He never says *no*. It's always, *OK, bebe, we go!*

The more he believes in me, the bigger a star he becomes," Lani says. "I've created the infrastructure for him to blossom, as big and as wide as he wants."

> "Creativity represents a miraculous coming together of the uninhibited energy of the child with its apparent opposite and enemy, the sense of order imposed on the disciplined adult intelligence."
>
> NORMAN PODHORETZ

Mars' Story

As the farm continues to grow, so does its crafts and product line. **Marseu Wesley Simpson** (aka Mars) is the go-to person for the farm's craft classes and general farm operations.

Much of Mars' innate talent for with working natural materials comes from her mother, a gardener and a healer who used the plants in her garden to care for her family. "I don't think any of us went to the doctor as kids, except for the shots required for school," Mars says. "From earache to you-name-it, Mom had something for it."

Mars grew up in Fiji, the Melanesian island nation that controls her home island, Rotuma. The Wesley family lived in Fiji's capital, Suva. While both the Fijian and the Rotuman people are Pacific Islanders, the culture of Rotuma is more related to the Polynesian cultures of island groups such as Tonga and Samoa. In traditional Polynesian fashion, the family practiced crafts as part of daily life.

"Everybody in the family wove place mats, fans, baskets to carry food—all those little things," Mars says.

Fiji has a history of British influence, so lavender was always around when Mars was growing up there, but she never paid much attention to it. It was just another fragrance, and she never heard of its being used to flavor food.

It was years and years later, long after Mars had moved to Maui, that she was first attracted to lavender. By that time, she had traveled far from her Pacific home with her husband, who works in aviation. A winter in Idaho persuaded her that they needed to head back to warmer climes, so in 1983, the couple moved to Maui. Mars met Lani Medina Weigert in 1985, and the two became friends as well as coworkers in the visitor industry.

Thus it was that Mars and Lani were together the first time they visited the lavender farm in Kula and met its charismatic founder, Alii Chang. Mars had seen a lavender wreath a friend got from the farm, and decided to order several for gifts. Craftwork at the farm in those days was a casual affair, and the wreaths were not ready when they arrived to pick them up. While they waited, Alii took Lani and Mars on the farm tour that would change all of their lives. "Lani and I were just in awe that someone had such a passion and wanted to share it with the public."

After spending a couple of hours with Alii, Mars knew there was a promising future here. "Oh my gosh," she said. "They're sitting on a gold mine, and they don't know what to do." But Lani and Mars were veterans of an industry

Mars Simpson: "Once we decided we were going to do it, it just took off."

whose job it was to connect visitors to exciting experiences in Hawai'i. "That's our specialty. We know how to bring people to this kind of thing."

They began to spend many evenings and weekends figuring out a business plan. Lani took the leap of faith first. She used her marketing skills to build a business that would support the two women, Alii and others who worked at the farm and its little shop. Within a year of Lani's career change, they knew that it was possible. Soon after, Mars left the tour business for the lavender farm on the mountain. She brought with her organizational and business skills, along with the love of handcrafts she'd learned from her youth.

"With our unique experiences and talents, once we decided we were going to do it, it just took off," Mars says. "The three of us just sit back in awe now at how far we've come."

"The list is just endless, the things you can do with lavender," Mars says of the farm's star product. Along with the popular crafts and the spectacular beauty of the location, the farm's food service, from lemonade to scones to full meals, has been a key to success. "Like any local thing, you bring in people, serve them food and you'll be a hit," she says, laughing.

"I'm mostly behind the scenes," Mars says. "But I also teach the wreath classes or train instructors. That's the fun part. I love doing those wreaths. That's my time to come out and get creative."

Because Alii has cultivated such a wide range of plants in addition to lavender, there are ingredients to work with all year round, depending on what's in bloom, what needs to be pruned, what's ready for harvest. For instance, since the protea, one of the farm's original crops, must be harvested in December, Mars put together a wreath class to use the blooms for holiday wreaths. Rosette-shaped succulent plants grow everywhere, along the edges of flowerbeds and driveways; like lavender, succulents thrive on the mist that rolls down Haleakalā. Tucked into a mossy frame, they make lovely living wreaths. While the succulent plants are recovering from their pruning, the lavender blooms, and it's time for pure lavender wreaths— purple, fragrant and long-lasting. At other times, herbs from the garden like thyme, sage, oregano, bay leaves and mint are woven into a fragrant herbal wreath that can be hung in the kitchen for use in cooking.

Besides lavender, many other blooms thrive on the grounds of Aliʻi Kula Lavender.

And wreaths aren't the only thing Mars can make with the farm's abundant plant materials. "Anything our customers tell us about, we'll research and find out if it's fun and fast enough for visitors to make," she says. Tussie-mussies are one example. Bridal parties who come for a luncheon as part of the pre-wedding festivities often want to do an activity together, and the traditional floral nosegays are a perfect craft for such occasions. Then there are Valentine's Day and Mother's Day— ideal reasons to sit down and make something beautiful and sweet smelling to give a loved one.

In Their Own Words: The Four Keys to Success

As we built Aliʻi Kula Lavender, we realized that every challenge was an opportunity for us, and knowing that kept us motivated to find the opportunities. Along the way, we also realized that four significant factors—crop type, collaboration, local marketing and value-centered business—led to our success. We learned these valuable lessons of aloha more by instinct than through formal business training.

The innovations and the values that guide Ali'i Kula Lavender start with, of course, owner Alii Chang's realization that he had to plant a **drought-tolerant crop**. This was a shift in paradigm for Kula, where farmers traditionally planted crops that required frequent irrigation from a water system that often runs dry. In this water-challenged environment, lavender was a whole new idea and a new opportunity. And for Alii, fresh from the humid jungle and florid tropicals of Nāhiku, lavender was an unfamiliar crop.

When Alii started farming more than 40 years ago, he noticed that farmers grew crops year after year, even though the crops didn't always do well. They continued to plant the same type of crop because family before them had done so. Since the days when he pioneered exotic tropicals, Alii has trod another path, always willing to take a risk and seek new ways. This is a lesson for farmers everywhere. It doesn't matter what the crop is, it's the shift in paradigm that's important, trying stuff you've never tried. Alii decided to grow a drought-resistant plant instead of what he knew, and therein lay success.

This lesson can be used by anyone, in any industry, or indeed in life: Look for opportunities that are appropriate to your location and environment that are outside the same old things that everyone around you is doing. Breaking free of a pattern of thought that no longer serves one's growth is a significant challenge. Will you stagnate? Or will you change by letting go of old ways that aren't working? Will you have the courage to shift old paradigms to new ones?

The second innovation was to collaborate. Our challenge was that we didn't have the money or the knowledge to create products, but **our opportunity was collaboration**. The fact that we didn't have any money—that's not unique! But collaborating within the community, and realizing that everybody here was a resource for us, was out of the norm. We collaborated with home-based businesses across the Islands. We didn't compete with them, we included them. They got more business than they ever dreamed of, and we got new products. Now we have

Lani Medina Weigert, Alii Chang and Mars Simpson: A partnership inspired by lavender.

more than 75 different products, none of which we make ourselves. We supply the lavender and the market; our community partners supply the know-how.

The second innovation offers this simple lesson, especially for farmers struggling to survive: Look for partners who can complement what you do. "It's a win-win for everybody," Alii says. "We have a very happy team going on. There's enough room for everybody if we all work together. There's a niche for all of us in agritourism, and it's beneficial for all if we work together."

The third innovation was to **market to the local community** in a way that was appropriate to Maui's culture. It doesn't matter how great the product is if there's no one to buy it. Along with everyone else in Hawai'i, we had learned, when the terrorist attacks of September 11, 2001 brought air travel to a standstill, how volatile the tourism business can be. So we made the decision to reach out to the local community and build a strong base of support. We began this unusual marketing campaign the first year Lani was on the farm by inviting 300 senior citizens to come for a tour.

Working through the active network of senior centers on Maui, we treated these elders to a visit, and they in turn told their families about this wonderful new farm and its products. Hawai'i has always greatly respected the words of its elders, and local people are also typically cautious. Perhaps

drawing on the ancient Hawaiian tradition of introducing oneself by reciting one's genealogy, the people of these Islands always want to know who you are, where you came from, and even what school you attended. By inviting the seniors, we introduced ourselves to a highly influential group at no cost to the farm. We hosted the seniors for tea and made special efforts to assure they had a relaxing visit to our unique farm. By the next year, our visitor count had risen to 3,000 through this grassroots word-of-mouth marketing campaign. While tourists from everywhere in the world are valued visitors to the farm, local residents provide the largest percentage of our business.

The lesson to be learned from this innovation: To build a strong base, look to the local market and find ways to invite influential folks to sample your product.

The fourth and most important innovation was the creation of a **value-centered operating**

Ali'i Kula Lavender regularly travels to O'ahu for the farmers market at Kapi'olani Community College. Below: welcoming visitors at the Gallery Gift Shop.

system based on aloha, the anchoring value of Hawaiian culture. While the word is well known, some of its meanings are not: Foremost, *aloha* means love, trust and friendship; in the context of the lavender farm it dictates the quality of relationships with people and with the land. Aloha is the barometer by which Ali'i Kula Lavender assesses performance and sets standards for excellence. All of our employees are trained in this philosophy, which turns out to be a very natural extension of hospitality and friendship.

Having aloha as the central value helps guide decision-making. For example, when sightseeing companies wanted to visit in big tour buses, the aloha we have for our neighbors made it easy for us to decide that it was not a loving thing to bring buses into this quiet, rural neighborhood. Because our business is value centered, rather than profit centered, the money was not even a temptation.

Other Hawaiian values also guide us. These values are among the many things that make Hawai'i special, along with its language, music, dance and art. The values that underlie everything we do at Ali'i Kula Lavender can be summarized with an acrostic of the Hawaiian word *Kuleana*:

Kuleana/Kūpono
   Being responsible and honest
Ulu/U'i
   Growing in beauty with all things
Lōkahi
   Working in unity with others; being cooperative
'Eleu
   Being proactive and taking initiative
Aloha
   To give and receive love, trust and friendship
Nānā
   To look, observe and care for
Akamai
   To be smart and clever

These values are the foundation of our business. They are not the typical ones you'll find in most corporate mission statements, but we have found them to be very appropriate and centering to our efforts. Of particular importance is the Hawaiian concept of lōkahi, which acknowledges the relatedness of nature and man and the importance of keeping life's forces in harmony. Aloha, another one of our fundamental values, brings people together by removing barriers and encouraging inclusion. Aloha is assured when we come from a place of gratitude and appreciation, working in natural harmony with all living beings. Great things happen when you bring people together—things that could not have been possible without synergy.

The Land Connection

> "He ali'i ka 'āina, he kauwā ke kanaka.
>
> *The land is a chief, humankind its servant.*"
>
> HAWAIIAN PROVERB

The powerful mandate to *mālama 'āina* (take care of the land) is one that emanates from our Hawaiian roots. That's why perpetuating farming and keeping open land is a priority at Ali'i Kula Lavender. In addition to lavender and a garden full of flowers and ornamental plants, we grow a vegetable/herb garden and a Native Hawaiian plant garden to provide other opportunities for cultural education at the farm.

Our two-part vision addresses our very high expectations for our products, entrepreneurial leadership and diversified agriculture:

Establish Ali'i Kula Lavender as the premier purveyor of unique, quality lavender products: Products that enrich the quality of life by evoking joy, rejuvenation, relaxation, renewal and serenity.

Establish a responsible model of agricultural tourism through education. Share the benefits of lavender and teach about its versatility through hands-on experience.

Our vision is to merge tourism with agriculture, while achieving sustainability. Sharing information about agriculture diversification, in both product development and services, with fellow farmers and the general public is paramount to initiating positive change and creating farm-related commerce. At Ali'i Kula Lavender, we strive to educate other farmers and pass on the knowledge we have gained in hopes of sustaining agriculture for years to come. We also promote entrepreneurial endeavors in culinary education, encouraging the chefs of the future to incorporate local farm-fresh produce and support a wellness lifestyle.

Lavender and its byproducts are a big draw at an open market held at Maui's Seabury Hall.

At Ali'i Kula Lavender, we think about agriculture as much more than farming crops—we are growing awareness, enhancing health and improving the environment. In this way, we think of growing lavender as growing life!

The Community Connection

Our commitment to growing our business while adding value to our community has created cohesive, financially viable partnerships. The joint ventures strengthen personal and professional relationships and our resolve to have a positive impact on an even bigger scale.

Leading up to the opening of Ali'i Kula Lavender in 2002,

> *"Happiness held is a seed. Happiness shared is the flower."*
>
> ANONYMOUS

we developed a business model based on inclusion. Rather than compete with our neighbors, we empowered them to grow as we grew. Forming partnerships with other local businesses has turned out to be a win-win situation for all. To help Maui's local economy, Ali'i Kula Lavender has established more than 25 partnerships with local businesses.

These include businesses such as Maui's well-known Roselani Ice Cream, which created the Lavender Mango Sherbet. Upcountry Specialties keep their home business growing by producing products such as Lavender Herb Dressing and Lavender Gourmet Seasoning. Tedeschi Vineyards, Maui's winery, created three types of lavender sparkling wine. Maui Tropical Apiary supplies Maui honey for the lavender-infused honey sold at the shop. Rainbow Ridge Farm, operating out of Launiupoko, Maui, partnered with us to make lavender coconut goat-milk soaps and lavender lip butters. Home-based Edamame Candles produces lavender-scented soy candles. We have partners on other islands, too, including larger name-brand companies such as Big Island Candies (Lavender Chocolate Brownies and Lavender Chocolate Truffles) and Kauai Kookie Kompany (Lavender Shortbread Cookies). Hawaiian Fudge Sauce Co. on O'ahu makes our Lavender Fudge Sauce, and Hawaiian Chip Co. in Honolulu makes our sweet potato chips.

More than 80 percent of the lavender farm's revenue comes from these value-added products. Without them, the farm could not thrive as it has, and the business community would not be sharing in the benefits of our mutual success.

Some of our partners are also neighbors. Jeanne the Bread Lady, who has baked homemade breads from her Kula home for more than 15 years, now makes more than 400 lavender scones each week, just down the road from us. "I've known Alii for a long time as a friend," Jeanne Pelekai says. "When they started the lavender farm, I told him I was making scones, and he asked me to make some for him." It took some experimentation to find exactly which type of lavender made the best scone, with Jeanne baking and the folks at the farm taste testing.

Now every Tuesday is "Scone Day" in Jeanne's kitchen, and while she and four part-time scone helpers make other kinds of scones for other clients, Ali'i Kula Lavender is one of her biggest customers. "He's a great client," Jeanne says. "It's been a really good thing for both of us. Alii is a phenomenal man. He has basically made a market for something that didn't even exist on Maui 10 years ago. And he's a good man to work with. He's great for the Kula community, because he uses a lot of products, and he'd rather buy locally."

> *"Opportunity is missed by most people because it is dressed in overalls and looks like work."*
>
> THOMAS EDISON

In addition to supplying one of the farm's signature products, Jeanne has some favorites of her own, like the Lavender Body Butter Cream and the Lavender Gourmet Seasoning, which she says "is great on fish or prime rib—it's outrageous!" And she shared a secret lavender trick she learned from the master himself ... Alii told her to put a sprig of lavender into a bottle of vodka. Jeanne says this makes for a great drink.

Another one of our partners who lives nearby is Jan Yokoyama of Maui Upcountry Jams & Jellies, which makes the Lavender Pohā Jam, Lavender Liliko'i Jelly, Lavender Strawberry Syrup and Lavender Strawberry Pepper Jam. Jan has noticed that, at Ali'i Kula Lavender, we go for broke! "When Alii and Lani get a hold of something, it's like *run*! It's been very good for us," she says. "They're very innovative, which makes you more apt to do more."

Working with us has allowed Jan to do what she likes to do, which is to stay at home on the farm and off the road. A Wailuku girl, she calls herself a "transplant" to Kula, where she started out growing roses. But roses were so perishable she decided to grow fruit, which is not as delicate, especially once it's in jars. Now she has a little kitchen on her farm where she processes all the things she grows and buys from local farmers—papayas, loquats,

Chef Paul Lamparelli prepares lavender cuisine at an outdoor cooking demonstration.

Surinam cherries, pohā, guavas, peaches, mangoes, black raspberries and strawberry guavas.

Jan helped develop our scone mix and now makes it for us, as well as our lavender lemonade and iced tea. And on our shelves are her delicious jams and jellies and the Lavender Strawberry Syrup that uses sweet Kula strawberries from another neighbor, Monden Farms.

It's another great win-win situation, in which each of us has taken the other's business to a higher level. For Jan, this means she doesn't have to go out as much to sell her products, and she says that "being kind of a backbone for someone else's business is nice. I like being here in this kitchen. I get to do my own thing and be part of making other people happy."

We know how she feels, because we feel the same way. The more we give, the more we have, and so our business and our friendships continue to grow.

The Experience Connection

*Kind hearts
are the garden,
Kind thoughts
are the roots,
Kind words
are the blossoms,
Kind deeds
are the fruit.*

JOHN RUSKIN

Our hopes and dreams are lofty; our standards for personal integrity are high. But the achievement of these aspirations happens person by person, through individual experiences that exemplify what we're all about. When Alii once said, "It is our social responsibility to take care of our communities and offer an experience that allows people to reconnect to the land, to each other, and to themselves," he was talking about putting into each guest's experience all of the values that we stood for. Our goal, first and foremost, is to create opportunities for visitors to feel, see, touch, taste and hear their environment.

We've worked hard to create a sense of place so that, from

the very first moment visitors arrive at the lavender farm, they know that they are somewhere special. A place that immediately conveys a feeling of warmth, beauty, vitality and well-being. We set the scene for what we hope will be a memorable experience for each guest on every visit.

An extraordinary site is part of the guest experience, as is the hospitality guests receive from the moment they arrive. We've put together a manual titled "Guide Book for Extraordinary Hosts" for each new employee. All of our objectives start with a full-fledged commitment to customer service. We know that customers are loyal when they are treated with sincerity and care, and that maintaining loyalty builds company equity. It all starts with our promise:

Popular Island recording artist Brother Noland serenades visitors at a concert venue with a view.

> *We promise to be extraordinary hosts, extending the feeling of aloha and hospitality to all. Creating excellence and quality in all we do to provide memorable and pleasurable 'Lavender Moments.'*

Our company's promise aspires not only to maximize customer joy, but also to give our guests a more enriching and meaningful experience of *Hawaiianess*, which is inherent in the nature of being hospitable to all. We make sure that all our employees are trained in this philosophy of hospitality and friendship.

We have gone out of our way to share these thoughts with other farmers in Hawai'i, hosting farmers from other islands who want to visit our operations and participate in statewide agricultural efforts. In 2007, Lani was elected the first president of the new Hawai'i AgriTourism Association. It establishes standards for the agritourism industry in Hawai'i and collaborates with agricultural producers and tourism affiliates to offer a high-quality, low-impact experience to visitors. Ultimately, the association supports local communities by promoting a farm experience, which then promotes Hawai'i as a destination.

The farm's Upcountry Paint-Out inspired a number of Maui artists, including Jan Shaner (this page) and George Allan (page 26).

Lani is also president of the Hawai'i AgriTourism Association, a board member of the Agricultural Leadership Foundation of Hawai'i, chairperson for Made in Maui under the Maui Chamber of Commerce, and chair of the Maui Economic Development Board membership committee. These outside community jobs keep Lani busy, but Alii and Mars support her in the outreach projects, because they believe it is important to promote Hawai'i's agriculture and preserve the state's open space.

The farm also participates in educating agricultural and culinary students, including elementary pupils. As part of the Ag in the Classroom program, we take plants and pots down to the county's agricultural park and work with youngsters, teaching them about growing things and about lavender. We actively promote agricultural careers with the Maui Community College Ag Department, and we work with the college's Maui

Culinary Academy on developing new products as well as donating a portion of all proceeds from our delicious Lavender Chocolate Truffle to the program.

Farmer groups from the Mainland who wanted to see how agritourism works in Hawai'i have come to visit us. We believe that the major components of the aloha experience are also applicable to agritourism farms on the Mainland—farmers only need to contemplate and define them in the context of their own farms and offerings. We suggest that they establish a "sense of place" for their farm, and staff the business with hosts who will ensure that every guest has a fantastic experience.

From our purple T-shirts and aprons to the lavender flags that mark new plantings to the lovely purple dragonfly packaging on all our products, we do everything we can to create that fantastic experience at Ali'i Kula Lavender. People leave here feeling good.

"Everyone who comes here is a guest to me," Alii says. "I'm having a party every day!"

Alii never seems to tire of showing his gardens to guests; to him, caring for this place is not work, it is creating beauty. Alii is always perfecting, always improving, always experimenting. Today, it's lavender products; tomorrow perhaps a unique Maui brand of olive oil pressed from the trees he's planted along the edges of the lavender fields. Then there are the bee hives that produce a naturally lavender-infused honey. And all of it contributes to the well-being of this island, to this farm on its slopes, and to all who come to marvel at its beauty.

By some magic, we came along at just the right time to catch the wave of interest in health and wellness, and the desire to reconnect with the Earth. We took the opportunity to ride this wave seriously and decided to do it with refinement and professionalism.

Today, more guests will arrive for a multidimensional experience, to feel the breeze on their skin, hear water trickling in our little fountain, see the textures and colors of the flowers, smell the scented air as flowers bloom. And we will go about our joyful daily business of greeting them and of caring for the ancient and noble lavender plant that has found a new home on Maui's majestic mountainside. ⌾

ACKNOWLEDGMENTS

Mahalo to my Grandma Lani and my mentor Howard Cooper from Hana who, without their wisdom and vision, I would not be who I am today. Thank you also to my dear and precious *'ohana* who have supported my endeavors through the years and been so generous of spirit and aloha: Edward Tremper, all my *'ohana* on O'ahu, Kaua'i and Moloka'i, Aunty Irene, Emma Veary, Ron Brown, Mark Kobayashi, David "Kawika" Saul and Koa Chang. Much aloha to our valued vendors who create our wonderful products made with lavender: Shirley and Hugo Buetler from Upcountry Maui Specialties, Jan Yokoyama from Maui Upcountry Jams and Jellies, Jeanne the Bread Lady, Denise Fleetham from Rainbow Ridge Farm, Nicky Beans from Maui Coffee Roasters, Chef Paul Lamparelli, Allan Ikawa from Big Island Candies and Lyle at Kauai Kookie Kompany. Thank you, Saedene at Sae Design, who created our unforgettable brand. And to my dear friends at Bunco: Roll the dice, and let the games begin!

—Alii Chang

I would like to acknowledge my dear friend and partner in lavender, Marseu Simpson, known endearingly as Mars. I am and will always be ever so grateful for our connection on so many levels. Thank you, Mars, for being the balancing element in our owners triangle at Ali'i Kula Lavender. I know at times it hasn't been easy, and as the unsung hero of the trio, you have been a marvelous embrace of Joy! You will always be family to me. Special thanks also to my other partner, Alii, with whom I have had such a unique kinship from the beginning, one that spans lifetimes between us. I will be forever grateful for the opportunity you afforded me to unveil my life's purpose and passion with the farm. It is with great pride that I send my deepest and warmest aloha out to the team at Ali'i Kula Lavender for their hard work and dedication that is such a huge reason for our success. Without you, none of this would be possible. *Mahalo* to Christie Fernandez, Jessica Hoecker, Johanna Jacintho, Tracy Jacobs, Jodie Kaea, Tehane Kahalehau, Deborah Leili, Cookie Pacheco, Joni Remington, Melanie Russell, Roberto

"Sonny" Silos, Toni Stanich, Jennifer Straw, Pomai Weigert, Michael McGuire, Joan Padgett and Edward Tremper. Much gratitude to Jana Wolfe for her writing expertise and heartfelt efforts. Finally, I dedicate this book to my grandmother, Emily Atkins Kaahanui, my mother, Katherine Leinaala Medina, and my father, Lawrence Ponce Medina. Without their unconditional love, support and wisdom, I would not be who I am today. *Mahalo* to my brothers, Rich, Larson, Ben, Nick, Bernie, and my sisters, Kiana and Charlotte, who through my entire life have shown me such unconditional love and support. To my children, Pomai, Joey and Aaron, who are the greatest treasures in my life—I live to love them—and to my granddaughter, Kamailemua Schillace. I burst in joy at the thought of you. To my biker guy, who has been an important part of both my growth and my love: Thank You—nobody gets me like you do! To all my family and dear friends: *Mahalo* for always being so generous in spirit, time and aloha. My life would never be as rich without all of you in it.

—Lani Medina Weigert

Special thanks to "Lavender Lori" Parr Campbell of Rocky Mountain Lavender in Missoula, Montana, for reviewing the chapter on growing lavender. *Mahalo* to Frank Kawaikapuokalani Hewett for translating *Pua Lavender*. Linda McCullough Decker of Maui and the folks at the Mission Houses Museum, Washington Place and the Hawai'i State Archives in Honolulu were all most helpful in the search for lavender's elusive early history in Hawai'i.

—Jill Engledow

Alii Chang is co-owner and Lavender Grower & Artist for Ali'i Kula Lavender. With his intuitive sense of placement and design in landscape, Alii won a Betty Crocker Award in 2004 for creating one of Hawaii's Most Beautiful Garden Landscapes. He resides at the lavender farm on Maui and is working to expand his crops to include olive trees and bee hives for the production of lavender honeycombs. He conducts educational cart tours twice daily at the farm.

Lani Medina Weigert is co-owner and Marketing & Promotions Director for Ali'i Kula Lavender. After 28 years as Sales and Operations Director for tour wholesaler Pleasant Hawaiian Holidays, she created and implemented a unique brand of agricultural tourism for Ali'i Kula Lavender, helping establish the farm as Hawai'i's premier lavender farm. Lani is president of the Hawai'i AgriTourism Association and a board member of the Agricultural Leadership Foundation of Hawai'i. She is also a professional speaker and owns her own consulting firm.

Jill Engledow has been writing about Hawai'i for more than 30 years. Her previous books include *Exploring Historic Upcountry* and *Island Life 101: A Newcomer's Guide to Hawai'i.*